GRACE WITH MEALS

*A Personal Experience of Cancer's
Discovery, Treatment, Recovery; & The Truth of Life
It Bestows*

R. Fred Zuker

Coskrey Biz

*Donna,
I hope you enjoy
This book about my
angel melody.
All the best,
Fred July 2022*

Grace with Meals
A Personal Experience of Cancer's Discovery, Treatment, Recovery; & The
Truth of Life It Bestows
(The Zuker Memoirs, Book 3)
Copyright © 2020 and 2022 by R. Fred Zuker, Ph.D. All Rights Reserved.

ISBN: 978-0-9719439-2-6

Library of Congress Control Number: 2020903630

Visit my website at HTTPS://WWW.AUTHORS.COSKREY-BIZ.COM/
ZUKER
First ebook publication via Amazon KDP: February 2020.
Published by Coskrey Biz, Sweeny, TX
HTTPS://WWW.COSKREY-BIZ.COM
Printed in the United States of America

Credits

THE IMAGES

The majority of images in this book are part of R. Fred Zuker's personal family photos. However, either Valerie or Wayne Coskrey of Coskrey Biz has tweaked the color and brightness balance and cropped a few of them to make them suitable for inclusion in this ebook. In some cases, the backgrounds have been altered or blurred to prevent identification of individuals not part of the story.

However, a few of the images require special credits.

The photo of Fred Zuker and Jason Zamora by Roosters, MGC in Pasadena, TX (5867 Fairmont Parkway, Pasadena, TX) is used with permission.

The collage using the head, neck, and throat cancer ribbon with images of Zuker was created by Valerie Coskrey of Coskrey Biz. The cancer ribbon was taken from Wikicommons and was created by an artist posting to Wikimedia. org (BML0309 at English Wikipedia "own work") and used according to the Wikimedia Commons license. HTTPS://COMMONS.WIKIMEDIA.ORG/WIKI/FILE:BURGUNDY _ AND _ IVORY _ RIBBON.PNG#/MEDIA/FILE:BURGUNDY _ AND _ IVORY _ RIBBON.PNG

Grace With Meals

R. Fred Zuker

Subheadings and Images listed by Chapter

Dedication
Image of Melody and Fred Zuker, November 2019, celebrating their 19th wedding anniversary

Preface
Image of Fred Zuker enjoying a meal in 2016

Introduction
Having Cancer Is Like Eating Alone When You Can't Eat

Chapter 1: Something's Wrong Here

Chapter 2: Speaking of Tongues

Chapter 3: Now What Do We Do?
Stage 1—Disbelief—Why Is This Happening to Me? What Have I Done to Deserve This? It's Not Fair!
The Tale of the Scan

Chapter 4: University of Texas MD Anderson Cancer Center—A Spectacular Medical Achievement
Who Was MD Anderson?
The Texas Medical Center
Section Reference

Chapter 5: Our First Visit to MD Anderson
Parkers and Pedestrians: Getting There Once You're There
Patient Support
Meeting the Team
Heading Home with the Knowledge that Cancer is Real. Now What?

Chapter 6: Biopsy

Chapter 10: Grace with Meals

Image of Melody Zuker preparing a holiday meal
Image of Melody Zuker's table set for a meal of celebration
Dysphagia–When Food Becomes the Enemy
Stage 5: Body Breakdown
G-Tube Button

Chapter 11: Radiation Treatment—Side Effects and Life Effects

Chapter 12: Family and Friends

Sonya's Story
A Lot of Help from Friends and Family
Death in the Family
What I Learned from 2014

Chapter 13: As Life Goes On

More on Side Effects
Working with Cancer
A Moving Experience
Starting a New Job
Image of employee ID card for Zuker when he started at Parker University
Are You Working Hard or Hardly Working?
The Feeding Tube Goes Away
Meal Mindfulness—Enjoy It While You Can
Image of Melody and Fred Zuker at a meal
A Taste of Honey: Food Stops Being the Enemy

Chapter 14: I am a Survivor, so What Does that Mean?

New Routines
Follow-up Appointments
Survivorship—I Want to Be on That Ship

Chapter 15: A Long Day at MD Anderson—Again

Am I Still a Survivor?
Having Cancer Means You Never Forget Having Cancer
Waiting to Go Back to MD Anderson
Back to MD Anderson

Selected References

BOOKS BY R. FRED ZUKER

The Zuker Memoirs Series on Amazon
Other books by R. Fred Zuker
Excerpts from *Standing Tall and Looking Good: One Soldier's Life and Lessons Learned from 1968-1971*
Excerpt from *The Dark Angel Turned Away*

About the Author: R. Fred Zuker, Ph.D.

Image of R. Fred Zuker, 2018

Dedication

This book is written for the millions of people who have an association with cancer. But the book is dedicated to my wife Melody who has been my steadfast caregiver on every step of our journey through the badlands of cancer. Without Melody's constant emotional support and active loving assistance, I would not have survived.

Thank you, my darling girl. I love you forever.

(Fred Zuker, January 7, 2020)

Image of Melody and Fred Zuker, November 2019, celebrating their 19th wedding anniversary

Image of Fred Zuker enjoying a meal in 2016

Grace With Meals

R. Fred Zuker

Table of Contents

R. Fred Zuker

Preface

Lucy made it all the way up the stairs by herself this morning. Lucy is our fourteen-year old Yorkie who weighs in at about three-and-a-half pounds. She is totally blinded by the cataracts that began to cloud her eyes two years ago. I mention this because this little dog's show of courage and determination reminded me of our recently completed drive from Dallas to Houston for me to revisit the MD Anderson Cancer Center.

A year and two weeks had passed since the last visit, and it was time for us to return to MD Anderson for the follow-up to my first survivorship follow-up examination. That one had included the usual blood work and CT scan with the addition of a chest X-ray. The chest X-ray was now routine.

One of my earlier chest pictures had revealed a spot that looked potentially problematic, but it was decided to keep an eye on it in case of any evidence of unwanted development.

We had been to MDA just two weeks before for a routine visit. The CT scan revealed a spot that caused concern. The MDA survivorship personnel wanted us to return for a follow up biopsy. Definitely not the news a cancer patient wants to hear. The period between the time of the CT scan on August 30 and our return appointment for the ultrasound and needle biopsy of the "left intraparotid lymph nodule" on September 13 was a waiting period of infinite uncertainty and anxiety. The trips back to MD Anderson for follow-up exams are always fraught with anxious anticipation.

The goal is to get the process completed, so we can expel the continuous undercurrent of anxious waiting that exists for a few days before the tests. When the news of the examinations is good, we can relax for at least a short while and let life return to normal. The return trip home after good news always seems much shorter. The days leading up to the Dallas-to-Houston trips are always reflective and tense.

I am a cancer survivor. The medical term for my cancer is oropharyngeal squamous cell carcinoma. In non-medical terms, it is a tumor at the base of my tongue. When it was diagnosed at MD Anderson in 2014, it had reached stage four. The stage of the disease was determined by the size of the tumor and the spread of the cancer to some of the surrounding lymph nodes.

This is the story of my experience from the initial discovery to now. It is a story of struggle and pain, of love and joy, of continuing challenges and the strength of many small successes. It is a story of shifting perspectives on truths and meaning, life and purpose, as well as family and friendships. And it is the story of what sustains a life worth living.

It is also a love story. My wife Melody spared no energy to lovingly accompany me through the terrrible days of my cancer discovery, treatment, and recovery. There is no better demonstration of love possible than her dedication to my cure and recovery.

Introduction

HAVING CANCER IS LIKE EATING ALONE WHEN YOU CAN'T EAT

If by some cruel circumstance you have lost your appetite, sense of taste, and ability to swallow[1], you will have greater appreciation for the experiences described herein. If, however, you have avoided such a loss, it will be difficult for you to understand the dispiriting depths of this form of misfortune.

Before going further, I must point out that the experiences that resulted in the above-mentioned loss in my life were created by the presence of a malignancy at the base of my tongue, a squamous cell tumor. Cancer.

The resulting chemotherapy followed by radiation and concurrent chemotherapy caused a successful reduction of the tumor to the point that it disappeared from the ghostly outlines of the CT and PET scans. Once the pre- and post-treatment scans were viewed, there were tears and hugs all around. For that, we are continuously thankful for the skill and experience of our physicians and others in whose care I was entrusted for those many months at MD Anderson in Houston.

But the side effects of the treatment created challenges that were explained to us but impossible to accurately imagine until they made their misery-producing appearance.

This is an accounting of the psychological, emotional, and physical reactions of one family to the discovery, subsequent treatment of cancer, and the recovery

---

1   Covid-19 patients and loss of sense of taste: After finishing *Grace With Meals*, the Covid-19 pandemic struck with full force. I learned early on that as many as 80% of patients who evaluate positive for Covid complain of the loss of taste and smell. (*Vanderbilt University Medical Center, Eskind Biomedical Library, May 21, 2020*) Members of our family and friends who have had Covid have confirmed the presence of this affect. All of them have remarked on how disturbing this aspect of the virus was to them. My sympathy goes out to them because I have been down that disappointing and frustrating path and know how debilitating it can be. The good news is that the people with that symptom found it temporary and regained most of their sense of taste. Some have said that the recovery has been only partial. My hope for them is that over time the full sense of taste will return. I feel certain that those who have experienced these sensory losses will have a new appreciation for the simple pleasure of tasting and smelling what they eat. It will be hard to take it for granted again.

period. I have tried to include my perceptions of the transitions I made to the fact that I had cancer.

The stages of acceptance of the presence of this disease is just the beginning of the story. If any cancer sufferer or survivor is asked to describe the worst aspect of the experience, they are hard pressed to come up with just one factor.

The progress of the cancer experience divides itself into three distinct parts: Discovery, Treatment, Recovery. Each of these phases has its own psychological, emotional, and physical elements. I have tried to describe each one in my experience, and how my wife Melody and I reacted to each of them.

I have included Melody's *Facebook* posts to family and friends about the progress of our cancer journey. Hearing her voice in these messages helps one understand how inclusive the support network can be and how helpful their expressions of love and support can be.

Anyone who survives cancer remains a cancer survivor forever. Cancer's shadow becomes part of your life. It doesn't have to darken everything. In fact, just the opposite occurs. The colors and textures of life take on a new vibrancy. Relationships are treasured more deeply. And the daily round becomes a welcome source of comfort, not a study in tedium.

To some extent being a cancer survivor makes you stronger. You know that cancer can be beaten. But those successes almost always come with a very high price. For most survivors the payment of the survivor mortgage goes on for a lifetime.

The reality of the effects that the cancer and its treatment have on a person is pervasive and permanent. For example, a survivor is always monitoring the body for signs that the original cancer has returned or that another form of cancer has arisen. You might call this "malignancy mindfulness." It doesn't mean that the survivor has become morbidly obsessed with the slightest body changes. Rather, you become constantly mindful of what your body is telling you, and you adjust what you are doing with your body accordingly.

The acceptance of that reality is an important part of the success of the survivor in the rebuilding of a healthy, positive lifestyle. My hope is that this book will help cancer sufferers, survivors, and their care givers and loved ones fully appreciate what a miraculous machine the human body is. And how, with the proper treatment and emotional support, a life after cancer can be more rewarding than the cancer sufferer could ever imagine in the throes of cancer treatment and recovery.

Cancer can be beaten and even when it is not, the heroism of those who are in the experience cannot be minimized. This book is a celebration of one family's ongoing relationship with one of the most fearsome forms of life on the planet.

For many years I have collected axioms and aphorisms that capture the remarkable miracle of life. As we went through the cancer experience, these nuggets took on greater importance to me. One of the most helpful axioms that I encountered during this time is:

> *Just to be is a blessing. Just to live is holy.*
>
> ~~*Buddha*

These words can give direction to all of us, especially those building their post-cancer- diagnosis lives.

As I worked on this project, I realized that my recall of all the details of my diagnosis, treatment and recovery was far from perfect. I have made every effort to ensure that my description of the medical procedures, reactions, and subsequent on-going treatment and examinations is accurate. My familiarity with the medical jargon and technical terms is bound to be wanting in some cases. I apologize in advance for these inaccuracies.

One reason for writing this work is to explain how the average person, who like me is untrained in medical disciplines, must deal with professionals who all work in the medical milieu constantly. The best of these professionals have a high sensitivity to making themselves understood despite the arcane nature of medicalese. From my experience, I suggest that an excellent thing to do is this when encountering the terminology and explanations that are often unintelligible if not translated from the medical jargon:

1. Take notes, lots of notes;
2. Ask questions;
3. Refer to those notes when you need to understand the medicalese and the direction for care.

R. Fred Zuker

Chapter 1: Something's Wrong Here

In the spring of 2014, I noticed that I was having some trouble swallowing. I had been having a lot of difficulty with post-nasal drip, coughing, and sneezing. I have been prone to serious head colds all my life. They are misery-making and usually last about a week.

I am reminded of the comedian I heard who said that she had a bad cold and went to her doctor to ask what she could do to relieve her symptoms.

She asked the doctor how long these painful, annoying symptoms would go on. The doctor told her that he could prescribe some drugs to help with the coughing and congestion. She should also monitor her fluid intake and get plenty of bed rest. He said if she did all these things studiously, her symptoms would end in about seven days. Or, she could do nothing, just gut it out. And then it will last about a week.

In the first days of cancer you want to do whatever the doctors tell you will beat the invader. It is only after the reality of the side effects of the treatment that you begin to think you might want to "gut it out."

My primary physician examined my throat and took the vitals, temperature, and blood pressure, and told me that I was suffering from the effects of allergies that were quite prominent in the part of Houston, Texas, where we lived. He prescribed some drugs, including steroids, that he told me would give some relief from the symptoms. The doctor told me that the post-nasal drainage was probably irritating my throat, causing my issues with swallowing.

I dutifully took the drugs and found some relief from the nasal dripping and sneezing, but the swallowing difficulty continued. I recall going to see my doctor at least twice with the same complaint and had the same response about allergies, with a suggestion that things would improve when the allergy-producing pollen abated and weather situations improved. I held out hope that it wouldn't be long before I had some real relief.

During this time, I attended a meeting in Seattle, Washington. I arrived the day before the meeting and got to my hotel rather late in the day. I went to the lobby restaurant for dinner by myself since I had not made plans to meet with any of my colleagues. I ordered something that I thought would be comforting, soup and a sandwich. As I tried to eat, I noticed with concern that I was really having trouble getting the food down my throat. My throat wasn't sore like I had often experienced at the onset of a cold or the flu. Rather, it was something else that was not in my world of experience. My mind began to misgive.

After I returned home, I continued to notice this swallowing problem. I found a small hand mirror and tried to get a look down my throat to see if it was inflamed, but nothing revealed itself to me. Finally, one night as I was standing at my bathroom sink, I reached into my mouth with my left index finger and felt as deeply into my throat as I could. I felt something on the surface of my tongue as far down as I could reach. I felt a lump on the left side of my tongue.

The lump seemed large to me. I recall it being rough to the touch and hard. It is remarkable to me as I recall this taking place that it did not feel like a catastrophic discovery.

I don't think I could believe it. Yet, I knew the symptoms were real. This thing I had discovered was not a result of some allergic reaction. It felt to me that I had discovered a tumor on my tongue. It was after this initial, rather distracted, mental-reaction process that the reality of what this probably meant began to coalesce in my brain. *This might be cancer!*

There was that word in my head. To most people the word means one thing—Death—impending, painful death. Very few people realize what a thousand-headed hydra this disease really is. Cancer comes in so many forms, has so many causes, so many treatment modalities, and so many reactions to the treatments, that it is a myriad of diseases with one inescapable, unimaginable, singularly devastating name.

This realization brings on Stage One of the cancer journey—Disbelief. *I can't believe I have cancer. No one in my family has ever had cancer on my father's or mother's side of the family. I've never smoked, and I have cancer of the tongue? It's not fair!* ("Not Fair"—Yet another descriptor of the first phase of Acceptance of Cancer process.)

This was part of my internal dialog.

Chapter 2: Speaking of Tongues

One of my first thoughts after this discovery was, *What a fucking irony this is.* Virtually my entire professional life has had to do with speaking communication. I was the guy known for his "pipes." People often told me that I had the perfect radio announcer's voice. My speech was largely unaccented despite my birth and years of growing up in the Deep South.

In fact, I had been the host or cohost of three radio programs. I co-hosted a movie review program for the NPR station at the University of California Riverside campus. The program was called *Focus on Film*. My co-host and I reviewed movies that were showing during that time and assigned them a rating between A and F. At the same time, I co-hosted a program on issues in education called *Education Today*. My co-host and I discussed current issues in education from K-12 through higher education in the region, the state of California, and the nation. Later my wife Melody and I co-hosted a radio program in Jackson, Tennessee, to help parents deal with parenting issues. That program was called *Parent Talk*. Melody is a Licensed Professional Counselor (LPC) and had done extensive psychotherapeutic work with tweens, teens, and families.

My primary employment for over forty years at the time of the cancer was in higher education. I began my career as an Office of Admission recruiter for Duke University, my alma mater. In that role, I was called upon to make presentations to groups of prospective students, their parents, counselors, and Duke alumni. I also spoke at college day and college night programs sponsored by individual high schools, school organizations, civic groups, and public relations organizations. Throughout my career, I was also a member of the teaching staff at every campus where I worked. I began by teaching self-defense for the Physical Education department at Duke. After I completed my graduate school training, I taught courses in philosophical psychology, clinical psychology, abnormal psychology, theories of counseling and adolescent psychology.

I was on my feet speaking all the time. My voice was a crucial part of the roles I played as a professional educator. As a result, the thought of what might be required to deal with cancer of the tongue took on an especially frightening and disconcerting aspect.

Chapter 3: Now What Do We Do?

STAGE 1: DISBELIEF—WHY IS THIS HAPPENING TO ME? WHAT HAVE I DONE TO DESERVE THIS? IT'S NOT FAIR!

After I discovered this growth on my tongue, I asked Melody one night to come into the bathroom, take a flashlight, and look down my throat to see if there was anything she could see that was amiss. She looked with the light and said she didn't see anything. But I knew there was something there. Hell, my own primary care physician had missed it with a tongue depressor—and had done so more than once.

After her careful inspection, I told Melody that I had felt something on my tongue, and I was pretty sure it was a tumor. I remember saying how ironic it was that cancer had attacked that part of me that had most to do with my work and livelihood. Melody's eyes widened when I used that word. She asked me what I intended to do, and I told her I was going to an ENT as soon as I could get an appointment. I tried to look unconcerned, but I knew she was worried. She had that knitted-brow look that I recognized immediately. I am sure she was like me, fearful of what we didn't know and what it would mean for our future.

It occurred to me that my Karma must be especially bad. I know my life had been far from error-free. There have been things that I have done that I regret doing, but this degree of punishment seemed to be a high price for my miscreancy. I identified this as Stage 2: The Acceptance of Cancer as the "Why is this happening to me?"—or to put it in different words, "What have I done to deserve this?"—phase.

I was done with my primary care doctor. He had missed what I thought must be a relatively easy thing for the trained medical eye to find, especially after my continuing complaints about my issues with swallowing. I decided to go to an ear nose and throat doctor that I knew near us. I made the appointment and must have sounded desperate since the scheduling person got me in for the next day.

Dr. Wilson, the ENT doctor, was slightly beyond middle age, with a welcoming smile. He asked me to tell him my concern. I told him about my issues with difficulty swallowing and that I had found this growth on my tongue deep in my throat.

He looked in my mouth with the tongue depressor and light. Then he put on a pair of latex gloves and felt down my throat with his finger. I could feel him touch the lower part of my tongue as the gag reflex began to trigger. He told me that he would look at my tongue and throat with a flexible laryngoscope. The procedure is called flexible laryngoscopy.

The procedure consists of the insertion of a flexible cable with a telescope at the end into the nose and down into the throat. He sprayed a numbing medication up my nose and told me to relax as much as possible because that would allow the tube to more easily navigate the narrow passages into my throat.

After scoping my throat and examining my tongue, he told me gently but firmly that I needed a CT scan (Computed tomography. Earlier nomenclature was Computerized Axial Tomography or CAT scan) of my throat and tongue right away. He gave me the name and location of a nearby imaging center. I called them on my cell phone as soon as I got to my car and made an appointment for the next day.

THE TALE OF THE SCAN

The scan procedure did not go smoothly, including the insertion of the IV for the injection of the iodinated contrast solution, which is used to improve the x-ray, CT images. I have never liked being stuck for blood testing, and now I would soon be subjected to sticks of many kinds, including blood tests, anesthesia, CT scans, PET (Positron emission tomography) scans, and chemotherapy IVs.

It has been said that the procedure of inserting an IV quickly becomes routine for the cancer patient. It has never been that way for me. I was told early on that my veins "rolled." I later was told that the rolling vein was a self-defensive reaction of the body to an attack on the vein to avoid injury. I don't know if that is true. The medical encyclopedias say they roll because they are not properly anchored during the blood drawing procedure *(Michon, 2018)*.

I learned from numerous experiences that the administrative types who check patients in for CT scans and are charged to insert the IV port before the imaging procedure are competent but not as skilled as the nurses. They may be trained phlebotomists, but I can't recall one who was able to establish the IV for me on the first stick. The result of almost every failed stick is immediate pain as the technician probes for the elusive vein. Failure also results in injection-site trauma and surrounding-area bruising. I learned to ask for the IV-insertion procedure to be done by a nurse.

I made it a strict practice to profusely thank all the blood-drawing personnel who establish the connection on the first stick. The laboratory technicians at the central MD Anderson blood collection point have always been expert at hitting their target on the first stick. I have also learned from experience that I had very bad experiences with blood draw taken from the bend in my arm that is the traditional location. The veins in my lower arm and hands are much more accessible. I was told that it hurts much more in the hand, but it is much easier to hit the vein the first time than to go through the process more than once after an unsuccessful search with the needle.

After we had established the IV connection, I was taken into the room where the CT scan device was located. It is a large tube of approximately seven feet in length. At the front of the device is a movable platform where the patient lies full length, face up. The technician in charge directed me to the table and positioned me as she wanted. She told me that I might feel a warm sensation as the contrast dye was put into my vein. She said that was normal and shouldn't be painful.

I lay down on the platform and the technician connected me to the suspended bag holding the dye. She said that if I had any problems, just to call out since they could hear me in the control room. I had heard that some imaging centers give the CT patients "panic buttons," squeeze balls, or intercoms to use if they became overcome with claustrophobia or some other disturbing sensation (*Revelant*, 2015).

She went into the control room and said over the intercom that they were beginning the dye injection. In just a moment I felt a sharp pain in my arm. I called out to the control room that I was having a problem. The technician came out, looked at my arm, and said that I had a "blowout." The IV had not been able to put the dye into my vein successfully, and the fluid had leaked out into the tissue surrounding the vein.

I thought, *DAMN. This is my first attempt at this, and it was fucked. Will this be the way it goes every time?* I had already concluded that I would be stuck time after time if this situation went the way I was pretty sure it would go.

The technician was able to reestablish the IV connection without too much trouble. She said that we would try it again, but that she would be sure and

control the flow of the dye to allow for
it go in more slowly and avoid a repeat of the blowout. The procedure began again, and this time I felt the warm sensation of the dye going into my vein but did not have the intense pain of the first try.

Then the platform I was on, which included the sliding bed where I lay, was mechanically moved into the tube of the device. Around the tube was the location of the imaging devices themselves. These built-in x-ray machines were arrayed in a complete circle around the opening in the tube. Since my scan was aimed at my head and neck, I only moved into the tube to about my mid-chest area.

Once I was located inside the tube, the noise of the x-ray machines inside the tube began. There was a whining, machine noise which was punctuated by loud booming sounds that surrounded me by 360 degrees. This went on for about ten or fifteen minutes.

It would have been helpful if the technicians had given me a little briefing on what I would experience. The noise was loud and frightening. Once it began, I assumed that was normal and I relaxed. I began counting in my head, one thousand one, one thousand two and so on. That helped me relax and gave me an idea of how long the procedure was taking. (My experience suggests that others might want to know what to expect. There are excellent information sites and videos on-line that will help the anxious CT or MRI patient. Google something like "claustrophobia during CT scan" for some useful information.)

I didn't have a good sense of the time I spent inside the machine because as I counted one-thousand-one, one-thousand-two and so on, I would be distracted and had to start the count again. After some time, the machine noise stopped, and the sounds of the rotating machinery subsided. I was mechanically pulled out of the machine.

The technician came in and said I had done well. She said the images they had secured were just fine. I was finished with my first descent into the CT scan "sunken place," a term from the excellent movie *Get Out*, where a victim was hypnotized and made to feel he was floating/falling in air in a dark, scary place.

The next day I returned to my ENT doctor for an evaluation of the results of the scan. As Melody and I sat down with him in his office, his demeanor spoke eloquently of the news that we had not yet heard but I knew was coming.

He told me that the results of the scan were concerning. That there was a mass located at the base of my throat that could be cancerous. He said that I should get an appointment with an oncologist who specialized in head and neck cancers. He went on to say that he had a good friend at MD Anderson (The University of Texas MD Anderson Cancer Center in Houston, Texas) who was a surgeon and was on the head and neck team. He had worked with her numerous times and had only heard praise about her work. He said he would call her immediately to find out when she could see me.

By the time we returned home, Dr. Wilson had left me a voicemail message saying that Dr. Amy Hessel, surgeon at MD Anderson, could see me right away. He left her number. I called immediately and made an appointment for two days later at 9:00 in the morning.

I began bracing myself for what I knew was the beginning of an ordeal that I couldn't even begin to imagine. It was as if I suddenly grew aware of a dream in which I was adrift on a large, dark body of water. I had no sense of location or direction. I was simply floating with darkness all around. I began counting the hours until I would make my first trip to the fabled, premier cancer center in America. MD Anderson.

R. Fred Zuker

Chapter 4: University of Texas MD Anderson Cancer Center—

A Spectacular Medical Achievement

WHO WAS MD ANDERSON?

What is colloquially called MD Anderson, or MDA, is the namesake of Monroe Dunaway Anderson. Anderson was born in 1873 in Jackson, Tennessee *(mdanderson.org, 2019)*, a small city located approximately mid-way between Nashville in the east and Memphis in the west. It is located adjacent to Interstate Highway 40, often referred to as Music Highway, connecting two of the most important locations of music creation and promotion in America. Jackson proudly claims as one of its native sons Carl Perkins, who wrote many songs, including "Blue Suede Shoes," one of the most enduring tunes of the nascent rockabilly, country music, and rhythm and blues revolution that would sweep the country in the 50s and 60s.

Anderson made his fortune as a banker and cotton trader. After moving to Houston in 1907, he realized great success in the cotton business. The company he formed with his brother Frank and brother-in-law Will Clayton became the largest cotton trading company in the world. To protect their wealth from estate taxes, the MD Anderson Foundation was created with capital in the sum of $300,000. An additional $19 million was left to the Foundation on Anderson's death in 1931 *(mdanderson.org)*.

The Texas Legislature in 1941 appropriated $500,000 to establish a cancer hospital and research center. The Anderson Foundation joined this effort and agreed to match funds dedicated to the hospital by the state. The Foundation agreed to this with the stipulations that the hospital be in Houston at the Texas Medical Center, which was another object of the Foundation's support, and that the hospital be named in honor of Anderson *(mdanderson.org)*. Before Melody and I first went to MD Anderson, we had already been introduced to Anderson and his support of education. Previously, for about five years we had lived in Jackson, Tennessee, where I had worked at Lambuth University. On the Lambuth campus was located the MD Anderson Planetarium.

The planetarium was built in 1967 with a grant from the Anderson Foundation, and figured significantly in the physics curriculum at Lambuth. The MD Anderson Planetarium also offered a schedule of educational programs that were open to the public. The planetarium still offers programs on a variety of space-related topics, including galaxies, astronauts, and space telescopes.

I had inquired about Anderson and was told by long-time Jackson residents that Anderson was indeed born in Jackson and had made his fortune in the cotton industry. Little did I know at that time that I would be the beneficiary of his support of medicine and research that was in large part responsible for the birth of the cancer center bearing his name located in The Texas Medical Center in Houston.

THE TEXAS MEDICAL CENTER

Anderson left Jackson and moved to Houston, Texas. He knew of Houston from his earlier days when he recognized the potential of the city for growing his cotton trading company. After his death, plans began to emerge to fulfill Anderson's dream to use his money:

> *"...(F)or the establishment, support, and maintenance of hospitals...to the promotion of health, science, education, and the advancement and diffusion of knowledge and understanding among people."*
> *(Alex Orlando, 2014[1])*

Medical and Dental educators in Houston gathered information on the creation of a "City of Medicine," coordinating the concentration of a center of many institutions all dedicated to patient care and medical research (*Orlando*).

In 1945, The Texas Medical Center was chartered by the state of Texas as a non-profit entity. Today, in 2020, the Texas Medical Center has 54 member institutions, 27 government agencies, and 27 non-profit health care facilities and has been recognized as the largest medical center in the world (*Orlando*).

Many great scholars have done their work at the Medical Center, as it is commonly called by the locals and those who use its services, including cardiac treatment pioneers Michael DeBakey, MD, and Denton Cooley, MD (*Orlando*).

Most recently in 2018, a research scientist at MD Anderson, Jim Allison, Ph.D., was awarded the Nobel Prize in Physiology or Medicine for developing a technique of cancer treatment that treats the immune system rather than the tumor.

I took a tour of the Medical Center with a group of corporate, education, and civic leaders in 2012. The tour was carefully orchestrated to make a strong impression on this group of visitors, some of whom came from quite a distance to see the Medical Center. The tour included visits to some of the hospitals and research facilities and ended with a sit-down, multi-media presentation on the Center.

I recall that the statistics on the number of square feet in the combined entities, the number of employees, the number of patients treated, and the amount of money required to maintain such a complex and leading-edge resources were astonishing.

There is no doubt that cancer detection, treatment and supplemental care are huge business enterprises with amazing income from treatment, foundations, research entities, and prolific donors who have been touched by the hospital's lifesaving services. These supportive donors come from all corners of the U.S. and the world.

MD Anderson is a truly world-wide resource for sufferers from cancer. During our years at MDA, we witnessed patients who were obviously, by their dress and languages, from many countries. These international patients were able to afford care from any provider in the world, and they chose MDA because it is reputed to be one of the best in the world. We were lucky to be in that number of beneficiaries of the MDA effect.

Endnote

[1]ORLANDO, ALEX, "BUILDING A CITY OF MEDICINE: THE HISTORY OF THE TEXAS MEDICAL CENTER," *TMC NEWSLETTER*, TMC.EDU: PARAGRAPH 4, 21 AUGUST 2014.

R. Fred Zuker

Chapter 5: Our First Visit to MD Anderson

My appointment with Dr. Amy Hessel, professor of the Department of Head and Neck Surgery at MD Anderson, was at 2:00 on Thursday afternoon, April 4, 2014. We prepared for our trip from our home in Clear Lake, which is about 25 miles from downtown Houston. One of the constant topics of conversation in Houston is the horrendous traffic. We wanted to give ourselves plenty of time to find our way to the hospital and to park, which we expected to be a challenge just because it was in the Medical Center, a huge bustling complex; and we were uninitiated. We also had to find the Head and Neck center in this huge hospital. All of this contributed to our sense of foreboding, not to mention this word overhanging the entire enterprise—cancer.

Traffic was relatively light at that time of day, which was in the two-hour window between rush hours. We had the GPS system turned on to help us with the navigation. As we turned off the freeway toward the Medical Center, the spires of the buildings began to come into sight. Rising above the others was a large building with a sign at the top level that read, "University of Texas MD Anderson Cancer Center." Even in the largest medical center in the world, MD Anderson stood out.

We passed the Hermann Park with its bucolic setting and scattering of runners and walkers on the perimeter track. We followed the directions to the main building located on Holcombe Drive. As we approached the building, we saw many numbered parking garages. One of the garages near the main building was number 10. I thought that if they had 10 of these large, multi-storied parking facilities, the demand must be enormous. I later learned that MD Anderson has over 20,000 employees.

As we made a first pass of the main building, we noticed many cars headed toward a porte-cochere and a sign that said, "Valet Parking."

Melody asked, "Valet parking?"

I said, "Hell yes."

I strongly recommend to patients and caregivers of patients who must use the parking facilities at large hospitals to acquaint themselves quickly and thoroughly with the requirements and logistics of parking and internal transportation.

MDA has a patient drop off location at the entrance doors. This is convenient, but be sure and have your cell phones handy to stay in touch. Also, remember to know the directions to your appointments, and to take all your paperwork and miscellaneous survival equipment with you.

At MDA the parking garages are huge and the means to make payment to leave the garage are complicated. Make note of the location of your vehicle in the parking garage. More than once we had to rely on the unlock lights of the car to help us remember where it was. Payment must be done inside the hospital buildings at kiosks. You must have your ticket (Don't forget to bring it with you and put it in a secure place, easy to find.) which you insert into the parking payment machine and then pay the amount which results in the dispensing of a token that must be inserted into a receptacle on a machine at the exit to the garage.

Don't lose the damned token. It is easy to do, and if you drop it in the car it is bound to go in that dark inaccessible place between the seat and the console. Murphy has taken care of that.

Once on foot in the hospital, you may have to walk for a long way before getting to your appointment location. Ask for directions as soon as you enter if you don't know the way. MDA provides large cart shuttles to go between buildings. If available, leave yourself time to take them to avoid a long walk. There are wheelchairs for those who are unable to make these long trudges. Always wear comfortable, stable, walking shoes, and carry a jacket or sweater. A large tote bag with easily accessible handles is helpful for carrying water, snacks, reading material, and notebooks with pens attached. We learned all of this by experience.

We turned the car over to the attendant and went into the large, well-appointed reception area. We asked at the information booth for the directions to the Head and Neck center. We were told Elevator C, tenth floor. Those directions would become imprinted on our brains after repeated trips to that area.

It is impossible to visit MD Anderson without being impressed by its size and level of activity. It is a huge complex with people moving in all directions. Great effort is made to ease the navigation to the many areas in the facility that must be found by patients making their first arrival for appointments.

I could not keep my heart from racing as we walked toward the bank of elevators. I knew what lay in store for us was going to be bad news. It was just a matter of how bad it would be and how long it would take for us to get to the point when we heard the word we dreaded?

We found the check-in area for all patients with appointments in the head and neck department. I had been assigned my patient identification number, which quickly became another bit of MD Anderson information that was burned into my brain. It is the practice at MDA that every time you move from one location to another, you are asked for your patient identification number and your date of birth. You are also asked to show your wristband ID that is often read by the bar code. I'm sure this is to ensure you are the right person and that all the information on treatment is entered into the Electronic Medical Record (EMR) system.

PATIENT SUPPORT

The administrators at MDA know how daunting it is for new patients to learn the ropes in a complicated place like this huge hospital. Add to that the disconcerting reason for patients to be there and the process can be overwhelming. To mitigate the potential for confusion and anxiety the hospital has established a patient support system that is very helpful.

Soon after we arrived, we were introduced to our patient advocate. She explained that her job was to help us solve any problems we encountered during our time at MDA. In addition to the advocacy program, there are programs designed to help with such issues as visitation, support for children, spiritual and psychological support, and patient education. Later we had need of our advocate to help us with issues related to medication and prescriptions. She was extremely helpful and let us know that she was there to continue to work with us until the problem was solved.

All the great hospitals in the U.S. with cancer centers provide some form of patient support. We strongly urge new patients and their families to find out what is available and make use of these resources. You will never know how much they can help until the time arises when such services are needed, and you find they are readily available.

MEETING THE TEAM

The receptionist located my record and directed us to a waiting area down the hall. All the waiting areas had identifying names of flowers. I think the first waiting room was the Dandelion area. We waited for quite a while.

After sitting for a few minutes, I noticed a board mounted on the wall by one of the doors with the names of all the doctors in this area listed and a notation of their availability. Dr. Hessel's name had beside it "one hour to wait." We came to learn that Dr. Hessel was in great demand and often ran late. She always apologized for keeping us waiting. The waiting did nothing for morale but only allowed for more focused catastrophic rumination.

We were finally asked to come into the examination area. My vital signs were taken—weight and blood pressure—and we were taken to one of the examination rooms. I took a seat in the barber-style examining chair. We waited some more. An intern came in and went over the information on my record. I had already listed all medications I was taking as well as over-the-counter drugs (non-steroidal anti-inflammatory drugs, "NSAIDS") and dietary supplements. I was asked if I was allergic to anything. I told her no.

Be prepared to answer those questions and to supplement the original information if anything changes; this applies to drugs, supplements, insurance, and present state of your health ("How would you rate your pain right now on a scale of 0—no pain—to 10—very severe pain?"). Cancer and the treatment create discomfort that is hard to measure on a simple scale. Be prepared to talk about your discomfort and how it affects you, and when it comes on, what you do to relieve it. That will help your care giver adjust treatment to better suit your needs (CREAKYSTAFF, 2018).

Dr. Hessel came in and introduced herself. She was young, enthusiastic, and energetic. She said she wanted to look in my throat with the laryngo-scope. Then she put on sterile gloves and said she would hold my tongue and reach down my throat to feel the mass at the base. I knew this would probably cause a gag response, but I was ready for that and would keep my throat as relaxed as possible.

(Someone putting a finger down your throat is not comfortable. Over the ensuing months and years, I would become accustomed to these diagnostic techniques. I didn't like them but understood the necessity.)

After these examination protocols, she said that based on my CT scan and what she could see with the scope and feel with her finger, I needed to have a biopsy of the mass at the base of my tongue. She told us that the mass was likely a Stage 4a, squamous cell carcinoma but that it was probably not the adenoid cystic type tumor which would be much more difficult to manage. There was the danger that the lymph nodes or salivary glands might be affected.

I would also be scheduled for a PET (Positron Emission Tomography) scan. The PET scan is used to check for cancers that may not be revealed by the CT scan. She also said that the treatment would probably consist of chemotherapy to shrink the tumor followed by radiation therapy.

She said the biopsy would be scheduled for as soon as her schedule would allow. Because of the location of the mass, it would be necessary for me to be under complete sedation. I told her that was fine with me. The biopsy was scheduled for three days later. I thought that the sooner we could have it done the better, since then we would at least identify the nature of this thing lurking at the base of my tongue and learn how to deal with it.

After our meeting with Dr. Hessel, we headed for meetings with the other two members of my team. I had not had the biopsy, but it was assumed that the information we would receive from the procedure would be consistent with what we expected the outcome to be.

Dr. Maserelli, my chemical oncologist, explained the chemotherapy process and the drugs that would be used to treat my type of cancer. She told us in general terms what we could expect the side effects to be. (This conversation did not prepare us for the ordeal of the chemo side effects that were to come.)

We were told that every patient has a different experience with the drugs. These cancer-fighting drugs are powerful. They can do much to save the lives of the patients to whom they are administered. But the side effects are punishing, causing many patients to be hospitalized during treatment. Some patients even decide they can't take the pain of the side effects and elect to discontinue the treatment.

There is a subset of research in cancer treatment solely dedicated to the mitigation of the side effects of the various treatments. Much progress has been made with more patient-specific dosing and correlated drugs dedicated to reducing the impact of the drugs.

It is true that despite these advances in alleviating side effects, as most cancer patients know, these drugs are in effect, poisonous. We patients steel ourselves to this fact by repeating in mantra-like fashion, "These drugs are killing the cancer." We just hope they don't kill us first on the way to the desired effect.

Next, we met Dr. Beadle, my radiation oncologist. Originally, I had been assigned a different radiation specialist. We learned that Dr. Hessel had personally asked for Dr. Beadle to be assigned to my case. We soon found out why when we told one of the technicians that my radiation oncologist was Dr. Beadle, and she said, "Great, Dr. Beadle is a rock star."

Dr. Beadle was also young and dynamic. She had a pervasive optimism that was profoundly welcomed by us. She explained that she would design a radiation program that would be determined by all aspects of my cancer. It would be mine alone, no cookie-cutter software off the shelf.

I stole a glance at Melody and could see the hopeful creases around the corners of her mouth. Dr. Beadle's nurse Gary was a no-nonsense guy who would be our guide through the radiation process. He was a twenty-plus year veteran of MDA and knew his way around this radiation stuff. He was a straight talker and avoided, when he could, the medical jargon and told us in laymen's terms what we could expect. His lecture before beginning radiation treatment came later. We'll never forget it.

HEADING HOME WITH THE KNOWLEDGE THAT CANCER IS REAL. NOW WHAT?

After the meetings we headed home using the HOV lanes, thereby saving many minutes of commute time. Our conversation was limited. I glanced at Melody out of the corner of my eye and noticed that she was uncharacteristically quiet. I said something to the effect that I liked Dr. Hessel; her attitude was no-nonsense but supportive and informative. I felt like I would be well cared for with her doing the surgery. Melody agreed and said she immediately liked her. We had information about the time and the preparation for surgery. Dr. Hessel had told us this would be a relatively short procedure. We agreed that the sooner we got this over the better.

My attitude at this point was one of continued anxious waiting. I wasn't particularly concerned about the surgery itself. The bigger issue was the outcome of the lab work done on the tissue recovered by the procedure.

Processing this information took some time. Understanding all the medical terms was challenging. Melody had taken notes during our conversation, which we still have. Her quickly written words belie the seriousness of the words we were hearing. What seemed clear to me was that I had cancer and we needed the biopsy to determine exactly what type of cancer it was; and when that was done, we could begin the work of attacking the tumor.

I had a hard time even grasping what this meant for the ensuing months and years. It was at this point that I reached Stage 3 in the Acceptance of Cancer—"One day at a time." I found that when I tried to consider the long-term implications of my condition, my mind just shut down. It was too much to contemplate. I told Melody that we had to begin thinking of this as a matter of what do we do next. Not a string of "what ifs."

I was sure that long-term speculation would lead to depression and a spike in anxiety that could only be harmful. Especially since I was convinced that long-term exposure to stress had been a factor in me contracting the damned disease in the first place.

We found that even doing research online about my condition could bring on a wave of anxiety. There is abundant useful information on the Internet, but when it comes to diseases it is all over the medical map because there are too many variables that can't be factored into an article or excerpt on Wikipedia or some other medically-oriented site.

Chapter 6: Biopsy

The day of the biopsy arrived, and we got to the hospital a little early to make sure we could find the waiting room with time to spare. I brought along my "MDA jacket" because the ambient temperature in the hospital was 72 degrees— but it seemed colder than that to me, probably related to my nervousness, (sometimes referred to as the "white coat syndrome" that often accounts for an increase in blood pressure readings at the doctor's office for even routine physicals).

I was taken back to the surgery prep area. My vitals were taken, and I went to a changing room to put on my hospital gown. I was taken to a curtained enclosure with a hospital bed, the rolling pole racks for intravenous fluids and all types of monitoring devices for blood pressure, heart rate and temperature.

I would soon become accustomed to this surrounding: one of my main concerns was getting a warm blanket to help me with the cold.

One of the nurses came in and started my IV. She was good, finding the vein on the first stick, and had me set up in a few minutes. She had me sign some paperwork indicating that I understood the potential dangers of sedation and issues related to DNR (Do Not Resuscitate) in the event of some emergency.

After the nurse left, Melody and I looked at each other and laughed. I knew immediately that she was thinking of my mother when she was being checked in to the rehab facility after a fall had required extensive hip surgery.

Mother didn't want to be there. She wanted to be in her house with her cats. My mother and father were both children of the Great Depression. As a result, my mother loved a bargain and always checked her receipts after making a purchase. So when the social worker at the rehab facility came to check her into the facility, my mother was listening carefully.

As the social worker went through several basic demographic questions, she chose her words carefully and asked my mother that if she was incapacitated and unresponsive, did she want attempts to be made by the staff to resuscitate her. Mother paused for a moment and said, "Does that cost extra?"

My brothers who were there, Melody, and I tried to stifle our laughter. Even the social worker looked aghast. After a pause, the social worker put down her pen and said, "I've worked here thirteen years and that is the first time anybody's ever asked me that question."

We smiled because we knew that question was quintessentially our mother.

Melody joined me in the prep room. The anesthetist came in and told me what would happen. He said because of the location of the biopsy site deep in my throat it would be necessary for them to run a tube down my throat through my nose. That did not sound like fun, but he said that I would already have a mild sedative in my bloodstream and would be relaxed. That sounded better.

Dr. Hessel came in to tell us that I would be going in soon and that she would see me when I was in recovery.

Soon they came for me and began rolling me out of the prep room, toward surgery. I told Melody "I love you" and gave her a big smile.

I felt pretty good because they had started the preliminary sedative. Melody squeezed my hand and gave me a look of love and concern that I still remember vividly. She said, "I will see you when you are back here."

The operating room was starkly white, with people moving with authority and purpose. They all had their jobs and they were going about their work with dispatch. The anesthesiologist came in and told me that they were going to install the nasal tube. That went smoothly. Then the anesthesia was administered, and before I knew otherwise, I was in another curtained area in the recovery room.

I felt a little groggy but not bad. My throat was scratchy but not painful. Melody was at my bedside and squeezed my hand again. What a relief to see her smiling, even if the smile was a little wan with her overriding concern for my well-being. The next part is somewhat muddled for me. One of the nurses came in to help me check out of the hospital.

According to Melody the nurse told her that she came into the recovery room where I was emerging from the anesthesia and said to me something like, "You're very handsome."

To which I said, "Yeah. I know."

I don't remember that exchange. But Melody said that she and the nurse and our daughter Ashley, who was there for support, exchanged glances and broke out laughing.

I finished dressing and then we left the hospital. I don't remember if I had to use a wheelchair, which is usually standard "operating" procedure (SOP) for a patient recovering from anesthesia.

This step was over and now it was waiting for the results. Dr. Hessel said it would be a couple of days before the lab tests results would be available.

BACK TO MDA

We had another appointment scheduled with Dr. Hessel in a few days. When the time came, we were at MDA a little early. The time of the appointment was 2:00 p.m. We knew that we would be waiting. By now we had heard from other patients who had been coming to MDA for a while that the MD in MD Anderson stood for "Most of the Day." That turned out to be true on many appointment days when we were scheduled for visits to as many as five different departments in a single day.

I had appointments at various times with my three primary MDA team members, each with their specialty: surgery, radiation, and chemotherapy. In addition, I would visit with Dietetics, Audiology, Dentistry, Sonography, CT scan, PET scan, Chemotherapy, Radiation Therapy, and lab blood draw. We appreciated the practice of the hospital scheduling staff to keep the various offices updated on our progress through the schedule, especially if we were running late due to a longer than anticipated wait at an earlier appointment.

Each time the door to the examining rooms opened and a receptionist came to call one of us in, my heart would thump a little louder—until I heard my name called. I then sprang into action not to keep them waiting, which was ironic since we had been cooling our heels for, in some cases, over an hour. I wanted to be a "good patient." (Sometimes referred to as a compliant patient. That is, one who did what he or she was told to do with little or no questions about why.)

I learned that it was good to keep notes on what we were being told and questions to be asked. In truth, the damned specter of the disease was so powerful that the thought of asking a question seemed to be challenging the awesome power of the illness to strike down anyone who questioned what the experts had learned about this villain. It was better to nod your head and say, "I understand," when, in fact, we were at a loss as to what would happen next. Melody was good about keeping notes and asking questions.

GETTING THE BAD NEWS: YOU'VE GOT CANCER

I knew what the results of the biopsy would be. They would confirm that the mass in my throat was malignant. What a terrible word! And it is almost always applied to cancer, although it could be used to describe any serious, possibly life-threatening illness.

The dictionary.com definitions for malignant are: *"Disposed to cause harm, suffering, or distress deliberately; feeling or showing ill will or hatred."* The word is derived from the Latin *mal* meaning "bad" and *nascor* meaning "to be born" *(Online Etymology Dictionary, nd)*. With apologies to George Thorogood, these cells were "born to be bad." And we have these cells living in our bodies concerned with only one thing—converting our body into their source of food and lodging. Unwanted guests if there ever were some.

Dr. Hessel confirmed our fears. The biopsy revealed that the mass in my throat at the base of my tongue was malignant. The official terminology is "hypopharyngeal carcinoma of the tongue." Melody's notes indicate the tumor was defined by the tumor staging system as a Stage T4A, which means a large tumor (larger than 4cm at its greatest dimension) with differentiated cells which are more normal and slower growing than undifferentiated cells which grow uncontrollably and are more invasive *(American Cancer Society, 2015)*. There was also some evidence that the cancer had moved (metastasized) into tissue in my throat and one of my lymph nodes.

Trying to decipher the medical terminology was difficult. We found that the information on the Internet should be heavily qualified because the articles and items speak in generalities lacking the specifics of an individual with the condition being investigated. The shorthand of all the jargon is: "You've got cancer."

Chapter 7: Beginning Treatment—Cancer Just Moved In

THE FACEBOOK DIALOG: EMOTIONAL SUPPORT OF FAMILY AND FRIENDS

Melody's Facebooking for Family and Friends:

(ACTUAL REFERENCE WITHHELD FOR PRIVACY REASONS.)

Most of you know but some do not. Fred has been diagnosed with base of the tongue squamous cell carcinoma. Because of the size of the tumor and the fact that it has spread to his throat and a lymph node it is considered stage 4. We were relieved yesterday to get the results of the PET scan which showed no further metastasis. He starts chemo Tuesday and will have it once a week for 6 weeks to shrink the size. He will have daily radiation after chemo for 6 more weeks. Please pray for us as we start this fight. We are determined and strong (scared and exhausted mostly.) I'll keep you all posted.

The above is Melody's first Facebook post to family and friends about my cancer and the treatment.

These posts show remarkable insight into the experience of cancer written by Melody for our friends and family. The posts are presented just as they were typed with no corrections or editing. They will be included at the places in the treatment narrative when they were sent. The posts are a more complete recounting of the treatment because Melody was sending them just as they happened.

My "chemo brain" recollection is flawed and mostly peppered with those events that resonated with me and entered long-term memory. Re-reading these posts reminds me how much of this journey I have repressed, probably as a self-protective device to save me from reliving all the pain—physical and emotional—that Melody and I endured.

CHEMO: THIS MAY HURT: BUT IT WILL BE GOOD FOR YOU

4/21/14

Chemo starts tomorrow. Fred's enjoyed Easter leftovers and strawberry short-cake. Hopefully the side effects won't be too harsh. Armed with homemade broth, saltines, and ginger ale just in case. So here we go....

The first round of chemotherapy consisted of six weekly infusions of four powerful drugs that were designed to have the desired effect on cancers of the head and neck, and they **all** had side effects: Erbitux, (blemishes, pimples) (*drugs.com*, 2018), Taxol (peripheral neuropathy), Cisplatin (allergic reaction, rash, itching/swelling, especially of the face/tongue/throat), and Carboplatin (nausea, vomiting, ear infection, hair loss) (*see drugs.com,* 2018, for a listing of each medication). We were given some information on side effects but not much detail. One example of literature from MD Anderson is the blog post, recently revised, concerning chemotherapy drugs and their side effects (*Bronson, 2014*).

MD Anderson Cancer Center has a website associated with a blog. Use the search term "Know More Be More" to access a blog with many helpful posts on types of cancer, information helpful to patients and to cancer survivors. Some of these are in printable forms that can be handouts or pamphlets. You can access years of blog posts using this link[i] at *mdanderson.org*[ii] for posts on throat cancer in 2015.

There wasn't much information on how the actual administration of the drugs would go. We weren't told how long to expect the procedure to take, or what, if anything, we should bring with us. I don't recall getting information on the other drugs that could be included in the chemotherapy cocktail. They often contained anti-nausea drugs, pain medication, and other drugs. (*American Cancer Society,* 2017).

We had to come in early for blood work to determine that all my blood levels were in the green for a chemotherapy transfusion. One of the primary measures was kidney function. That had to be good to process the injection of the cocktail of poisonous anti-cancer drugs along with the anti-nausea and pain-controlling chemicals.

The chemotherapy area at MD Anderson has a large waiting room with comfortable chairs, some of which are loungers with the footrest that extends as the back is lowered for stretching out full length. It was also possible to get a blanket because, as always, the ambient temperature was in the low 70s.

We had learned that we needed snacks, puzzles, iPhone chargers, newspapers, and sweaters or jackets for the chilly effect of the air conditioning.

A small handout that gave an overview of the chemotherapy protocols would have been very helpful.

When my name was called, we were taken back to an area that had numerous draped infusion sites complete with bed, infusion liquid, and the portable metal pole pouch-carrier where the drug pouches would be hung during the treatment.

The nurse came in and introduced herself. She brought in her IV kit to start the IV by finding a vein and installing the hook-up devices for the drug drip. The nurses were all adept at finding my roly-poly veins and getting me started. Over the course of six transfusions, I don't think I had the same nurse more than once.

The nurse would bring in the drug pouches that all had identifying stickers attached. The nurse for that day's treatment would make sure that I was the right person for this drug pouch by checking my wrist band and asking me the standard questions. (She had already checked my blood chemistry levels. If my kidney function was sub-par, they would start me on a saline solution to make sure I could process the drugs going into my body.)

It was always about the same, but I suppose my attitude was different each time, hoping for a good stick and a relatively fast drip of the drugs. Occasionally an alarm would sound in my area, and a nurse would hustle in and check the connection of the drug pouches to the drip port in my arm. The nurse would turn off the alarm and usually make an adjustment to the drip device or the pouch. They would usually look at me and smile indicating that things were fine. That always made me nervous that something was going wrong with the damn drip and I would have to start over or do something else I didn't want to do. I was always mightily relieved when the pouches were empty, and the nurse came in to unhook me.

This became the IV/Chemo drill. The entire process initially took over five hours. It would later take only about two to three hours. I had a TV in the room, and we would occasionally turn it on to watch the news or *Gunsmoke*, depending on our mood.

Sometimes we would be there over the lunch hour and I would order some food that would be brought to us. I would eat while the drugs were dripping. We thought it was interesting to be eating while these drugs were going into my vein. This is when I first began to think of grace with eating. At least I was still able to eat. It was later that eating became almost impossible.

4/25/14

Sorry for not posting sooner. So, Fred seems to be tolerating the chemo pretty well. He's had sometimes when he felt really bad (last night). has had very little appetite, and the rash has started on his chest and back. Good news is that he has not been nauseated or had any stomach issues so far. We have both gone to work yesterday and today. Fred has come home early (believe it or not) which tells me he is tired. But he is taking it all in stride. Tuesday is the next chemo infusion treatment. It should be shorter this time (4 hours rather than 6) And we are going to go to the MD Anderson satellite clinic here in Clear Lake rather than drive to the Med Center. I am tired but feeling less anxious now that treatment is underway. Love to you all.

My attitude toward this process was interesting to me: I didn't like any part of it. The sticks for blood work and the IV were always—literally—painful either physically or emotionally... or both. I never got used to sweating out the IV stick, always hoping this time it would be routine with only "one stick and ready to go."

My attitude toward each administration was influenced by what had happened the previous time. If it had gone well with no problems and reasonable comfort, I felt good about the latest procedure. If there had been problems or it took a lot longer than expected, then I would have more trepidation about the next one.

As I lay in the bed early on, I would check the progress we were making with the amount of drug in the pouch gradually decreasing. I would have the internal dialog about the benefits of the treatment. This was before the side effects began to arise. Later when the side effects were so uncomfortable, I told myself *This was the price one pays to stop the progress of this thing, this cancer that had appeared in my body.*

These chemo days were exhausting. The waiting was draining, primarily due to the anxiety that permeated the building. We watched other patients sitting in the reception areas as they read a book, checked their cell phones, or just stared straight ahead seemingly oblivious to their surroundings. I called this the "Cancer Cocoon." Sometime the weight of all this was too much to face, and the empty stare, while I turned inward, was all I could manage. At-ease conversation was difficult during all this cancer-concentrated activity.

This Stage 4 in cancer adjustment is what I call "Treatment Trauma." After a couple of times through the chemo process, I became more or less accustomed to the drill. It was always relief to see the fluid levels in the chemical pouches bottom out. We knew that after each infusion there would be reactions, some good and some bad.

Every cancer patient reacts differently to their treatment. Some of the interventions have more challenging side effects. Most people have heard of the hair loss and nausea that often accompanies chemotherapy. There are other side effects as well: insomnia, rashes, muscle soreness, constipation, diarrhea, and fatigue.

In addition, there are the psychological effects of the treatments. Each round of chemotherapy and radiation therapy, for me, were somewhat traumatic. Each one of the treatments is a test of physical stamina and coping with the psychological stress. I don't think it is possible to overstate the impact of stress on cancer patients and their caregivers. As soon as one treatment is over you begin to count down to the next one.

All the while you are measuring the amount and severity of the side effects. You also begin to do what the caregivers of the seriously ill do in measuring day by day how the patient is doing. Consider this dialog for example. When the caregiver is asked how the patient is doing, the caregiver is likely to say, "He had a good (or not so good) night (or day)."

Cancer patients do the same thing, although we tend to break the day down into smaller increments—Waking up (How do I feel?); Getting up (Are there any new aches or pains?); Look in the mirror (Oh shit, is more of the hair gone, the rash worse or better?); and so on through the day. We patients are measuring our day almost hour by hour, meal by meal, bowel movement by bowel movement. It will wear your ass out. That is why, when we *are* in relatively good shape—with minimal pain, discomfort, and/or anxiety—we want to keep it that way and tend to stay immobilized, afraid to do just about anything for fear of upsetting some somatic mechanism that is in delicate balance but could tip at any time.

I'm not sure the comparison of the cancer treatment to a battle to overcome this enemy that has invaded the body is that helpful. After all, the cancer is part of my body. Certainly not a welcome part, and one that may very well kill me. But a failing heart or a massive infection may have the same effect. We don't talk of heart disease as an invasion or a battle. We do what we can do and what medical science has deemed as the best way to interfere with the pernicious process of the cancer's progress.

If the interventions do their intended job, we sufferers will have more time to live. We hope that the extended time we have will be cancer-free and that we will be able to enjoy a life that is pain-free and meaningful to us and our loved ones. Hell, our lives should be that way without cancer.

SIDE EFFECTS: THE RESULTS HAD BETTER BE GOOD!

We were warned that the drugs would have side effects. All of us have heard of the side effects of cancer treatment, hair loss, nausea, vomiting, diarrhea, and others. One of the drugs (Erbitux or Taxol) that I was scheduled to receive had the side effect of a skin rash that could be serious. We were warned of this in advance.

The full bloom of this rash was spectacular, even to our medical team at MD Anderson. And they have seen just about everything these drugs could dish out. We were told at the outset of chemo that if I had some reactions, like the rash on my face and neck, that the drugs were working on the tumor. That gave me some solace since I soon found out that the drug was kicking my ass. I hoped it was doing the same thing to the damned tumor.

4/28/14

Here's the latest – Fred has the rash which is now on his chest, back, face, and neck. It isn't painful yet, but we've been warned that it probably will be as treatment progresses. We were also told that the rash is a good sign that the chemo is working...so we'll take it. Also, he has been nauseous off and on...and eating is not his favorite thig (hard to swallow, no taste, and no appetite.), but I am tempting him regularly with tasty concoctions. Second chemo infusion is tomorrow and we are relieved that week one is in the books. Fred is keeping a good attitude; he is a true fighter. We had a great weekend. Actually took in a movie (Transcendence, it was really interesting and thought provoking.). We both went to work today (I'll admit that I didn't get much work done) and are happy that Ashley and the girls are here to support. I'll keep y'all posted. Much love.

After the third round of the six treatments, a rash began to appear on my back, shoulders, and neck. It then spread to my face and scalp. It was there but not very noticeable and not very uncomfortable. After the fourth treatment, the rash on my face had transformed into a livid, red burn. The heat from the burn was so intense I felt as if I had been subjected to the worst possible sunburn that Destin, Florida, might create without any of the pleasures of that lovely beach. We called our chemotherapy oncologist and she asked that we come in for a face-to-face, so to speak.

5/3/14

Well guys, it's getting kind of rough. The rash has turned into something resembling leprosy. I have never seen Fred more miserable. He can't leave the house and doesn't feel like doing much. We have been watching a marathon of House of Cards on Netflix. I don't want to leave him alone so we've neither one gone to work. The doctor called in an antibiotic and a gel that doesn't help. Debbie downer here...sorry. Maybe it will be better tomorrow. Asking for good vibrations, prayers, God's healing grace or peace. Something?

When my doctor entered the room and saw my face, I noticed with chagrin that her face registered not just concern, but outright surprise. She regained her composure and after performing an examination, said that my reaction to the drug was the worst she had ever seen. Note that this is MD Anderson where, presumably, the greatest possible range of reactions to the various treatments would be registered. I was in a league by myself. I could be a poster boy for chemotherapy reaction. There might even be a picture of me in the classic textbook on oncological dermatology under the heading of "Damn."

The dermatologist that we were seeing was so impressed with my rash that she asked us if it would be alright for her to bring in her interns to see firsthand my condition. I thought, *Why not? It might help them if they see a patient with a similar outbreak.* The interns came in. I believe there were three of them. They introduced themselves and took a long look at my face, back and so on. They politely refrained from saying something like, "Holy shit." We appreciated that.

It was so bad that when we walked the halls of MD Anderson from one appointment to another, I would receive a shocked stare of wonderment at my condition from other sufferers or those others whose business brought them to the hospital.

After I had seen several of these stares, I told Melody when we returned home that I had received three or four PMFs today.

She looked at me quizzically and said, "PMFs?"

I explained that when people saw my face the look, or double take, that I received reflected what they must have been thinking: *"Would you look at that poor motherfucker."*

To give you a more graphic description of my condition, I refer you to the Star Wars movie, *Episode One–The Phantom Menace*, featuring the rubbery Jar-Jar Binks character and one of the most colorful villains of all time, the Sith lord, Darth Maul. You may remember him. He brandished with deadly effect the double-bladed light saber and had the brilliant red face complete with horns, and Mike Tyson-type tattoos. The color of his face very closely matched the color of mine. I did not have the tattoos, the horns, or the sharpened, pointy teeth; but I could have been mistaken for one of his earthly cousins. It was that bad.

5/6/14

Starting infusion three as I type. Thankfully the doctor started oral and topical steroids yesterday giving Fred some much needed relief. The Dr is keeping the dosage the same so we'll see how this round goes. Halfway through chemo after this? (Then radiation…but we won't go there yet.) I'll keep you posted. Love you guys! Fred say hi.

During the first three weeks of the chemo treatment, I continued to go to work at Texas Chiropractic College. I had been serving as the interim president for about seven months. When I received the cancer diagnosis, I informed the Board Chair of the college that I needed to cut back on my duties. The decision was made that I would move to another assignment and a new interim president would be named while the search for a permanent CEO was continued. My colleagues were more than solicitous. They were kind and supportive, offering me continuous good wishes and offers of help with work and anything else I needed that they could provide. I continued working until the side effects made me tired, and I began to think that the dramatic rash that I had would scare any unsuspecting students or visitors who might cross my path.

CHEMO CONGRATULATIONS—NOW WHAT DO WE DO?

5/15/14

Well hello all, Sorry I haven't posted lately. Fred had his fourth infusion on Tuesday and we went into MD Anderson for a check-up today. Although his rash has improved the doctor was very concerned about it. We told her how much worse it has been and she said that he should have been in the hospital. Oh well!! Poor thing *. She now has prescribed a daily steroid to help him through the rest of the treatments. She wants to see him every week because of the rash. He is starting to lose his hair...but he has a lot...so he still has hair for now. One of the chemo drugs, Taxel, is the one causing the hair loss and he only has two more of those infusions. She also told us that he will have to go on another type of chemo for the six weeks of radiation. We didn't know this until today. Good news is that

Image of Fred Zuker about midway through treatment

he will have three weeks before the chemo/radiation starts back. He has been feeling bad, but is still going into work a few days a week...you know him! He is struggling with very little appetite and is still losing weight. No worries..I'm finding it on me *. Seriously, he is supplementing with high calorie smoothies and Boost. The tumor is still getting smaller which is great, of course. So...we are marking off the days on the calendar...day by day. Thanks for all the thoughts and prayers and continued support. Love you all, Mel (emoticons removed at *)

Roosters, MGC in Pasadena, TX (5867 Fairmont Parkway, Pasadena, TX); used with permission.

Image of Fred Zuker with his favorite barber Jason Zamora
(image is not part of the Facebook post)

We were told that one of the side effects of the treatment would be hair loss. My hair is unusually thick, so when it began to fall out, it was not too noticeable at first. The problem developed when I tried to find some respite from my flaming face. The prescription ointments that I was given all caused a stinging reaction. The only solace I found was from good, old petroleum jelly, which I liberally applied, especially at night. The petroleum jelly would calm the worst of the burning sensations that came with the fiery face. I soon discovered that when I woke up in the morning my face would be covered in the hair that had fallen out onto my pillow during the night and stuck to the petroleum jelly. I looked like a troll with a badly trimmed beard that extended from above my eyebrows to my chin and neck. Trying to remove this combination of hair and jelly was difficult and demoralizing.

Within a few hours of discovering this disconcerting mess I made an appointment with my Roosters stylist, Jason. I had been going to him for almost five years. I knew him well and loved the way he took care of my hair and gave me the shampoo and hot cloth treatment that was so soothing. I told him, "Take it all off. I can't stand it anymore." He did just that and we took a picture of him and me standing by his stylist chair with my shorn noggin glowing in the artificial light. He gave me a hug and a blessing. I still miss him.

The skin rash that I developed was so dramatic that the doctors thought it best to cut back on the Erbitux, which they thought was the drug causing the skin reaction. We continued the chemo sessions all the way through the full regimen.

We did have some relief by being allowed to go to the MD Anderson-affiliated hospital near our home in Clear Lake, Texas. That saved us the long drive to the Medical Center, which was always a source of some anxiety because the uncertainties of Houston traffic could never be predicted.

5/23/14

Hello guys.

Fred has been having a very difficult week. His skin reaction flared up again to the point that they held off on the Erbitux chemo this past Tuesday. During the appointment at MDA yesterday with the chemo doctor, she became so concerned that she sent him to the dermatologist there. The dermatologist was alarmed as well, but sent us home with new meds (steroids, antibiotics) and ointments (stronger hydrocortisone and antibiotic cream) They did a culture as well. We should hear back on that today. We were cautioned to go to the MDA ER if anything worsened. Relieved to report that he is somewhat better today. Fred's daughter, Julia, has been here helping out immensely but left this morning to go home to CA. Appointment this morning to shave off what's left of the hairs...it's time. So...that's where we are. Thanks for all the positive energy, thoughts, and prayers. XOXO

5/29/14

OK..yesterday was the last day for the big guns chemo. We would be celebrating if things were not escalating. This reaction has taken on a life of its own. It has spread to his eyes and causing him much pain. Now a new outbreak on his neck, back, scalp and arms. Chemo doc thinks it could be a reaction to the Taxol, because they held the Erbitux the past 2 weeks (the drug that causes this reaction.) She sent him to the dermatologist last Thursday and we returned today. Dermatologist is so baffled she did 3 cultures and a biopsy on a pustule on his arm. She also sent him to the ophthalmologist there at MDA. That dr. prescribed antibiotics for his eyes (weeping pus-like). We should hear tomorrow on the cultures and Monday or Tuesday on the biopsy. We are back at MDA on Tues. to see the dermatologist and ophthalmologist. All docs say it is the worst reaction they have seen. Poor Fred...very weary of all of this. He has been through it. Prayers, thoughts, positive energy, and magic requested. (heart emoticon) to all, Mel

6/3/14

We went back to MDA today to follow up with the dermatologist and ophthalmologist. Results of the cultures were all negative for bacteria or virus. The biopsy indicated that it is caused by the chemo. His eyes are better, but he continues to suffer with his skin. The PET scan is next Thursday which will show how much progress has been made and what he radiation will have left to annihilate. He is quite weary...but has been very brave. Thanks to all of you.

6/7/14

Well I'm so happy to tell you all that Fred is feeling better! He is now 11 days out from his last chemo treatment for this round and his face is finally clearing up. He is still dealing with his chest, arm, and hand breakouts but they are healing. His appetite is better...he has had blueberry pancakes, chicken, and a whole burger today. Next week is full of appointments to prepare for chemo/radiation and the PET scan which will tell us how much progress he made from chemo. I will let you all know the results.

6/15/14

Thought you guys would like to see how good Fred looks about 3 weeks out of chemo. He has developed a blood clot (DVT) in his leg for which he is self-administering Lovenox shots. He begins both chemo and radiation tomorrow ... So here we go

6/17/14

Some of you already know the wonderful news!!! PET scan showed that the CANCER IS GONE!!!!! We are so elated we don't know where else to dance a jig!!! (6 smiling emoticons removed) It was so cool—Julia and Kai were there with us when we all heard the news. The doctor said it was the best response she could have possibly hoped for and then some! He will still have to complete the chemo/radiation to ensure that all cancer cells are gone and won't return, but we definitely have a second wind now. Woo Hoo!!!!!

In addition to the skin rash and hair loss, I had other side effects including terrible muscle soreness in my shoulders. It was so painful that we called my MD Anderson doctors and asked what this meant and was there anything I could do to alleviate the symptoms? They said we should come to the MD Anderson emergency room for an examination.

We loaded up and headed to Houston. After checking in at the ER, we were taken back to an examining room where the attending doctor said they wanted me to have blood work (more sticks), a chest X-ray to eliminate the possibility of lung or cardiac involvement and a CT scan (I can't remember if we did this or not.)

After the results of these tests came in, the doctor said everything checked out negative. She recommended I take extra strength Tylenol. I thought, *Really? After all these tests the best they can do is recommend that I stop by my local Walgreens for an over-the-counter (OTC) NSAID (Non-Steroidal Anti-inflammatory Drug) for pain?* (Note: many people consider all pain killers to be NSAIDS. Not so. Tylenol is not but is an analgesic. But this was my initial thought at the time.)

I suppose it is at least a form of CYA, but Tylenol didn't do anything to relieve the pain. I went to my chiropractor at TCC, and he told me that probably because I had lost so much muscle mass in my shoulders that the nerves were more easily aggravated. He suggested that when I went to bed that I put a small pillow under my arms to take some of the pressure off my shoulders.

I tried the pillow that night since the pain was worse at night. That minor adjustment did have the desired effect. I was able to sleep through the night without the aggravating pain that would have me on the floor trying to find a position that would not have me writhing and using words that would have made my basic-training drill sergeants blush.

SLEEP BLESSED SLEEP

A suffering person hopes to find some surcease from pain in sleep. In fact, many of the opioid drugs cause a sufferer to fall into a drug-induced sleep. The resulting drug hangover can be harrowing.

One aspect of this treatment that was so dispiriting was the difficulty with sleeping, especially when the rash was in full, fiery display. So many times I would get into the bed with my face covered with petroleum jelly goop, which limited my possible positions in the bed to those that did not touch my face. I would arrange the covers for maximum coverage because my sensitivity to cold was often intense. Then the muscle pain would often ensue. I was also often concerned about stomach issues related to constipation and hemorrhoids.

If anything, being in bed increased the problem of dealing with pain, because there were no distractions from discomfort like television, conversation, etc. I was alone with the suffering. My pain tolerance is pretty high after years of painful, but not serious, injuries from football. But this was different. These pains came from a pain place that I didn't recognize.

I tried to stay away from the pain meds, but the doctors told us not to let the pain "get ahead of you." In other words, if you waited to take the pain meds until after the pain was entrenched, it was much harder for the meds to give the hoped-for relief.

This brings me to another admonition. Don't take going to bed and going to sleep for granted. Even those of us—and there are many—who suffer from various forms of insomnia, having pain be the sleep preventative is different. It isn't the constant internal dialog of an overactive brain but the screaming pain receptors that you can't turn off that keeps the light in your head shining. When one settles into the covers without pain, pause the thoughts of what you should have said to your pain-in-the-ass office coworker long enough to be thankful that you are in a bed of comfort, not distress. Just putting your mind in that place may make it easier for sleep to spread the comfort over you.

WHERE TO GO WHEN YOU CAN'T GO?

The chemo nurses told us at the beginning of the injections that I was receiving a cocktail of drugs in the IV formula. Some of the chemicals were designed to mitigate the nausea that often proved too difficult for the suffering patient to withstand so that the chemo had to be paused or stopped altogether. Many of the medications for pain had a significant likelihood of causing constipation. Recently a television commercial had touted the benefits of medication to mitigate the effects of OIC (Opioid Induced Constipation). Based on my experience, I would say that such anti-constipation treatment would be important to anyone requiring chemotherapy for cancer.

One of my most upsetting side effects of the chemotherapy regimen was constipation. This is not an easy topic to discuss, but virtually all of us have had the experience of constipation and know how miserable it can make you. One of my best friends was philosophical about pooping.

He said, "There is nothing more undervalued than a good shit."

I once heard a comedian say that he had such a good dump that afterwards his pants fit him better.

Melody and I learned the importance of taking this issue seriously when I became so backed up, with cramping and in serious pain, that we resorted to home-applied enemas. The relief that came after the enema, the desired effect, is indescribable.

There are no words to properly thank Melody, my angel caregiver, for how much she helped me during those times of almost unbearable distress.

Constipation is often complicated by the attendant condition of hemorrhoids, sometime called piles. They are caused by the straining to pass uncooperative feces. There are two types, internal and external, neither of which is welcome.

I found both types to be painful before, during, and after attempts to defecate. The presence of hemorrhoids makes defecation even more difficult and painful than just constipation. Plus, there is the presence of blood on the toilet paper, in the toilet bowl, and on the feces.

Damn, I believed constipation and hemorrhoids combined were a misery in one of the most graphic and distressing forms imaginable.

The hemorrhoid situation reminds me of the joke about…

(T)he obstinate, unpleasant, and uninformed person who was prescribed suppositories for his presenting condition.

One week later he came back to the doctor's office furious. He told the doctor that what he had prescribed didn't work at all. The doctor asked him if he had followed the directions for the medication.

The patient replied angrily. "Of course, I did, what do you think I did, stick 'em up my ass?"

I came to the literally painful realization that whatever the combination of softeners and laxatives that works for me is what I should do.

Forget the experience you may have had with these substances pre-cancer, because after these invasive and destructive treatments, your body is very different. Your diet and activity level are also probably greatly changed from pre- to post-treatment. Your body's chemistry has changed.

There are drug store and grocery store shelves full of laxatives and stool softeners. (When I first heard this term, I thought it had to do with making more comfortable seating options.) Our great MD Anderson nurse Gary, who worked with Dr. Beadle, told us in a pre-radiation meeting with about twenty-five soon-to-be radiation patients and their loved ones, to be careful not to get into a difficult situation with bowel movements. He suggested one or two of the many products one may select to help with this problem. He said that even if a patient is on a mostly liquid diet it is important to poop at least every other day. We left the presentation with notes on several topics from diet to laxatives, to skin potions to help with the radiation effect on the skin, and more.

The thing I wish Gary had been more emphatic about was that we, the patients, had to find a system to avoid constipation that worked for each of us individually.

In my case of tongue cancer and the damage to my salivary glands by radiation, I couldn't manufacture enough of the saliva that is crucial for swallowing and digestive processes. As a result of the weight loss that came with these changes, I was assigned a feeding tube. (More on that later.) But that also had dramatic effect on my digestion, caloric intake, and mental state related to eating and pooping.

It is crucial that cancer patients find the combination of treatments, diet, and regimen that works. It is best to plan on pooping every day. It is also desirable to take the products to help you poop at night with the plan that they will work in the morning. But don't be afraid to get up at night if that is when you have the call. Don't be overly dismayed if you have accidents or create clean-up necessities. This is simply part of the process. The body will recover, but it will never be the same as it was before the cancer treatment.

I remember another comedian who said that…

(A)n older gentleman was discussing the ailments of age with some of his buddies.

He told them that he had no trouble with peeing or pooping. He said that every morning at 6:30 sharp he takes a leak with the flow like a rope. Then at 6:45 he takes a massive poop with no trouble. He said the only problem was that he didn't get out of bed until 7:00.

Everybody is different, and your body will be new to you after cancer treatment. As always, every cancer patient should be mindful of all the directions from their caregiver team. But don't hesitate to ask questions and do research on issues that are of concern to you.

No doubt "Dr. Google" drives many health care professionals to distraction with inaccurate or not applicable information. But this type of research may serve the good purpose of helping the patient frame the questions about their treatment that will save time in their interaction with the treatment team.

AND ANOTHER THING

As I neared the end of the first round of chemotherapy, I noticed that my ankles were swelling, especially the left ankle. There was no pain, but when I mentioned it to Melody, she said we should tell the doctors. When I did that, I could see their foreheads knot a little and I knew that meant that this was not a good development. They told us that one of the other side effects of chemotherapy was the formation of blood clots. The doctors said they wanted an ultrasound of my legs to determine if there was a clot. We scheduled the procedure for the next day.

A blood clot sonogram is not a bad procedure. It basically involves having technicians pass a transducer over the skin that has been covered with a gel to allow the easy passage of the device which delivers a sound wave into the tissues. The sound waves generate an image of what is going on inside.

The sonogram of my legs revealed the presence of a blood clot (thrombus) behind my right knee. I had had surgery on this knee in 1998 after running (against medical advice) the Boston Marathon. I mentioned that to the doctors, but they were unimpressed with my running prowess and said that type of surgery probably had no effect on the formation of the thrombus.

A thrombus in the leg is known as a deep vein thrombosis or DVT. The great danger of this situation is the possibility of the thrombus breaking free to travel through the bloodstream. This floating mass (embolus) may reattach and create a blockage (embolism) (*Chemocare, nd*). If a blockage occurs it could trigger a stroke, heart attack, or pulmonary embolism. All of which are bad. If the embolism blocks a smaller blood vessel, such as in the lung, you have a pulmonary (lung) embolism which can be deadly (*Chemocare, nd*).

One of the primary treatments for an embolism is a blood thinner (anti-coagulant) to prevent further formation of clots. There are many medications of this type, some of which are advertised on television. They are Heparin, Warfarin (Coumadin), Lovenox, and Xarelto. Because of the thinning of the blood, any surgery—including dental activity—had to be carefully planned to avoid excess blood loss (*Chemocare, nd*).

I was prescribed Lovenox. The difference with Lovenox is that it is administered subcutaneously, by injection. I learned to give myself shots in the skin around my stomach area. The injection device was a fine-measurement needle loaded in a spring-operated syringe holder. If I did the job correctly, the injection was virtually pain free. There were many times when I didn't get it quite right, resulting in some bruising. It was a blood thinner, which meant that it didn't take much to cause a bruise.

I did not look forward to those daily injection events. It was one more damn thing to worry about, but I did it dutifully.

We had to wait for a clear ultrasound before discontinuing the Lovenox. I was later put on the tablet form of the blood thinner Xarelto, which made life a lot easier. After about two years on this drug, I received a clear ultrasound test and my hematologist took me off the Xarelto. That was another good day.

R. Fred Zuker

Chapter 8: What I Have Learned—Stress Can Kill

The basic functioning of the human body is still a mystery in many areas. When you add to the basics of human physical functioning an aberration like cancer, the mystery becomes even greater. One of the most difficult aspects of the psychology of cancer for the patient is the randomness of being selected to be the host of this evil addition. We now know that there are some genetic templates that predispose persons to certain types of cancer. Undoubtedly there is more about the genesis of the disease that we will discover as the technology improves.

In my mind, a major factor in the etiology of the disease is chronic stress. I have been through my adult life as a reasonably calm-appearing person. Even when things around me are in tatters or emergency, I seem to be able to operate with relative ease. That belies the turmoil inside.

I am a highly competitive person, and that has been a blessing and a curse. I love a challenge, but I often berate myself for not achieving the blue ribbon even when the odds are virtually prohibitive of such an outcome. The result of that world view is relentless planning and preparation with rumination on why I didn't do better if I do not have an unqualified success. I am certain that the resulting elevated level of stress has taken a toll on my body as well as my psyche.

One of the few advantages of the cancer experience is the reframing of perspective on what is and what is not important. Damn few things are important, and that realization becomes quickly crystalline when you are waiting for CT scan results that will tell you about life and death. The resulting axiom is this: As worries begin to course through the brain, pause the thought train and then let it resume its journey without you. Keep things in perspective at a low volume. Deal with them as your resources of all types allow, and then move on to some ice cream. Another way to put it is: Worrying doesn't help. Unknit your brow and mindfully relax. Tell yourself. "I will do my best and stop hurting myself."

Another technique I have found that comes in handy in many stressful situations is a breathing technique used by the Navy Seals. When I was in basic training at Fort Campbell, Kentucky, the drill sergeants told us about controlled breathing while squeezing the trigger on our M-14 rifles. The Navy SEAL approach, also called "Box breathing" or "Tactical breathing," as taught by the drill sergeants, is useful in all manner of situations and easy to remember; it has four steps of four counts each:

Step 1 – Inhale (from the stomach up) to fill the lungs for a count of four.
Step 2 – hold your breath for a count of four.
Step 3 - exhale and empty the lungs for a count of four.
Step 4 - hold your lungs empty for a count of four.
Repeat until you feel your body relax and your mind quiet.

It has worked for me while driving to stay awake, on airplanes in turbulent weather, and in CT scan tubes while the X-ray machines are thumping. I've also done simple counting to help calm my nerves and assist in going to sleep. The technique helps quiet the noise in the brain when that motor won't turn off that's replaying all the stuff you are trying to still, so you can get some rest.

Chapter 9: Radiation Therapy—A Complicated, Burning Love

COMPLEX PREPARATIONS

Before beginning radiation, there were several things that had to be covered —dentistry, audiology, and swallowing. Procedures, screenings, and protective devices were used to keep the damage from the radiation as low as possible.

DENTISTRY

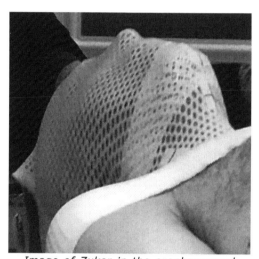

Image of Zuker in the oropharyngeal mask for his radiation treatment

I was scheduled to see the MD Anderson dentist about the effect of radiation on teeth. My teeth were examined for any problems. I have always taken good care of my teeth. I have had regular checkups and cleaning for a long time. My mouth is full of crowns and fillings going back to my misspent youth of sweet treats from my Alabaman mother and grandmother and inconsistent care of my teeth.

Fortunately, I received a good report from the MD Anderson dental team. They told us that any potentially problematic teeth must be extracted before radiation. The head and neck radiation would weaken the dental structures, making any dental procedures dangerous. I was given information on keeping my teeth strong after radiation.

The dentists gave me tooth trays and fluoride gel to use daily after radiation. I made sure that I used the fluoride treatment toothpaste at least twice a day after radiation and have continued to do so religiously. The threat of cancer pitfalls makes a compliant patient out of even the most recalcitrant sufferers.

R. Fred Zuker

FOR MOVEMENT RESTRICTION (IMMOBILITY)

I was also fitted with a mouthpiece to be used during radiation treatments. We were told that I would wear this device for every radiation treatment. It was designed to minimize the radiation damage to the tongue. These devices were made to resemble either a tongue depressor or elevator. In my case the device was made to hold my tongue down and immobilize it. This is apparently standard procedure for all patients who undergo head and neck radiation therapy.

To make it fit my mouth as completely as possible, my mouth was filled with a warm putty-like substance and I was told to bite down and hold it until the putty hardened. They took this mold and used it to make the specially fitted mouthpiece. This was not like the mouthpieces I used in football. This thing filled my mouth and made it difficult to speak or swallow when it was in place. It was made of a plastic/polymer material that was hard.

When I returned to pick up the device, I tried it and found that it filled my entire mouth once it was in place and secured by the teeth indentations that were built in from the impression. It was almost impossible to breathe through my mouth with the mouthpiece in place. This gave me an unpleasant, choking sensation. I had to consciously breathe through my nose and do so carefully. The mouthpiece added to a sense of claustrophobia and initially made me prone to a choking panic response.

The head and neck radiation treatment require that the patient's head be as still as possible. To this end. a pretreatment cast of my head and shoulders was taken with the overlay of a plastic netting that was applied warm and pliable. It was shaped to my head and shoulders and allowed to dry into a closely fitting mantle that was then secured to the radiation table by snaps. Ensnared in this device I was prevented from moving my head more than a few millimeters. I also wore my custom-made plastic mouthpiece that filled my mouth and made it virtually impossible to swallow.

After a few treatments, I learned to make myself relax once the mouthpiece was in by using my breath control techniques, counting in my head once I was strapped down and couldn't move.

AUDIOLOGY

Another possible side effect of radiation was a decline in hearing function. Melody has long said that my hearing must be defective because I seem to lose myself in reading the newspaper or a book. I admit that I am often distracted by work, or projects, or just plain wool gathering.

Her comments reminded me of the joke about...

(T)the guy who says, "My wife accuses me of not paying attention to her when she talks. At least, that's what I think she said?"

To check me for hearing affects from radiation, I went to the audiology center at MDA and had a hearing test to set a base line that could be used to determine if my hearing was deteriorating. The test went smoothly.

The technicians told me that I had some hearing loss at a higher pitch. Subsequent visits to the audiologists indicated a continuing hearing loss but nothing that was classified as significant.

I know that in the presence of background noise, such as present in a crowded restaurant or cocktail party, my ability to hear conversational discourse is limited. Thankfully, I can still hear a live band or skillful DJ making music. As Bill, my sainted father-in-law, was fond of saying about the loss of physical capability, "I may have trouble walking but I can still dance."

HARD TO SWALLOW – DYSPHAGIA

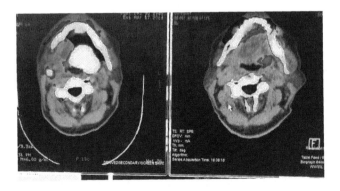

Image of Zuker's cancer on PET scan

6/22/14

Just got to thinking that family members might like to see the dramatic picture we took of the before and after comparison of his PET scan results. The yellow parts on the left are the tumor and lymph node. We are still completely overjoyed and in shock! He has completed the first five radiation treatments and chemo infusion. He is feeling icky but his face looks great!

Another side effect associated with radiation treatment of the tongue and the tongue area is difficulty swallowing. The medical term for this difficulty is dysphagia.

Swallowing is one of those things that we take as a given. We put food in our mouth, and we are supposed to be able to swallow it. Sometimes when we are embarrassed, surprised, or nonplussed, we may gulp and choke a little; but most of the time we manage to get it down.

The truth of swallowing is that it is a complex process involving several structures and processes in the mouth and throat.

Image from inside the radiation therapy control room showing Zuker on the computer screens as he is lying on the table waiting to be irradiated

Production of saliva or spit or spittle is another of those bodily functions that happens on its own. We've heard the expressions "whet your appetite" (whet—to sharpen), "mouthwatering;" and, we all know, "drooling." All of these are related to the production of moisture by the salivary glands (*UW Health, 2019*).

This moisture is really the beginning of the digestive process. Chewing food and mixing it with saliva form a bolus, a mixture of food and saliva that is pushed to the back of the mouth and pushed down by the tongue. The voice box (larynx) closes to prevent the mixture from entering the airway (*UW Health*).

This is important because if the food enters the airway, that is known as aspiration. It is highly uncomfortable and may lead to a variety of unwanted

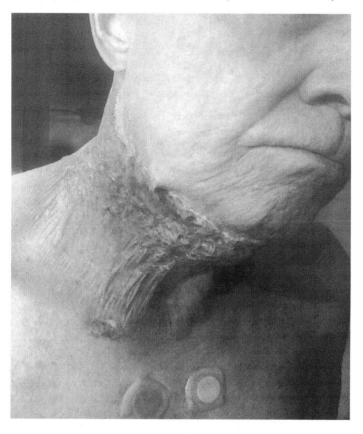

Image of the radiation skin damage on
Fred Zuker's neck

consequences such as pneumonia (*UW Health*).

Once the food passes the larynx, it enters the esophagus and travels to the stomach (*UW Health*).

Once the swallowing mechanism is compromised you never take eating and swallowing for granted again. Eating is now often accompanied by coughing, clearing the throat to avoid "getting something caught in one's throat."

7/3/14

Well, Fred is almost halfway through radiation and chemo. He is really feeling the effects…fatigue, sores in his mouth and on his tongue, loss of appetite and no sense of taste. He has lost quite a bit of weight and will probably have a feeding tube after next week. Eating is hard and there is no way to keep his nutrition up to take the rest of treatment without one. He is still taking the Lovenox shots for the blood clot in his leg, but those symptoms have improved. All in all our spirits are still high and feeling still so relieved that he is winning his battle. Please continue to pray for him as he endures this hardest phase of treatment.

Every time I went in for another radiation treatment, I would obsess over the possibility of choking from the inability to swallow once I was strapped down with the large mouthpiece in place. I made it a rule as part of my pre-treatment ritual to swallow at least once with the mouthpiece locked in under the netting. It was no easy feat, but I managed to make it work with total concentration on swallowing the little bit of saliva that I managed to create.

The actual radiation treatment only lasted about a minute and a half. I counted one thousand one, one thousand two, and so on until the treatments were over. I could hear the radiation delivery system circling 360 degrees around my head. On either side it would stop and make a clicking sound. I imagined that each click was the radiation pulses hitting me from both sides, taking out the damned cancer cells, but also hitting some innocent bystanders along the way.

My excellent radiation oncologist showed us on her computer the landscape of the radiation treatment she had designed for me. She said that this was an elegant radiation plan and that the strongest beam would be directed at the tumor site with as little collateral damage as possible. However, some damage to surrounding tissue was unavoidable. Indeed, it was helpful to make sure any stray cancer cells would be caught in the obliteration of the radiation charge.

The first few weeks of the five times weekly regimen of the total of thirty-three radiation treatments wasn't so bad. Melody had found for me an effective skin cream that seemed to protect me from the skin damage that was the usual result of exposure to concentrated beams of radiation.

I refer to the skin damage as a "burn," but the damage done to the skin by radiation treatment is not a burn, per se. The skin reaction is caused by the X-rays that damage the outer layers of a patient's skin. It is estimated that 95%

of patients receiving radiation treatment will develop some form of radiation dermatitis. The severity of the reaction will be determined by the strength

Image of Zuker wearing his Heisenberg hat and sunglasses made famous by the character Walter White, the cancer sufferer in Breaking Bad

of the radiation dosage, the number of treatments, and the sensitivity of the patient's skin to the radiation. The severity of the reaction is measured by the symptoms and divided into four grades ranging from Grade 1—faint redness and skin peeling—to Grade 4—death of skin cells and deep skin ulcers. My reaction was Grade 4.

I did learn that radiation directed to the head and neck is more likely to result in radiation dermatitis. I have avoided, so far, one of the most frustrating symptoms, which is the appearance of skin damage weeks, sometimes years, after cessation of treatment. This development is called radiation recall *(Barrell, 2018)*.

The last two weeks of the radiation sessions were tough. By that time the skin under my chin down to about my clavicle was badly damaged from ear to ear. I was given a miracle dressing by the dermatology team that took the burning sensation away for sleeping. But getting into the shower and having the water hit those compromised areas for the first time was a breath-taking experience—and I don't mean that in a good way. The skin on my neck was badly compromised, so a stray application of a band-aid to help hold the dressing in place resulted in a square of skin being removed when I tried to gently

Image of A Collage of Photos Made of Zuker during the Cancer Years of Treatment and Remission

remove the dressing. That place stayed raw for the next couple of weeks under the constant bombardment.

After my neck healed, I discovered that the beard on my neck was completely gone save for a few stray hairs that seemed to disappear a little later. I calculate that I have saved about a weeks-worth of time by not having to shave the same facial dimensions that were required pre-treatment.

The skin on my neck looks normal to the untrained eye, but it is scar tissue resulting from the deep ulcerative damage that the radiation caused.

After this experience, I had a much greater appreciation for the heroism of the first responders and thousands of individuals who dealt with the nuclear reactor disaster at Chernobyl portrayed with chilling effect by the actors in the HBO series of the same name. Radiation damage, even in a highly controlled environment like MD Anderson, is serious business.

7/23/14

Five more radiation treatments to go!! Monday is last chemo. He is hanging in there and doing pretty well. Feeding tube is helping and he has already gained 4 lbs. Good news abounds. He's looking forward to a pizza and some beer. That may be a little while. He's feeling very fatigued, sore mouth, no saliva, bad taste… all normal.

7/31/14

Last day of radiation! Now on to recovery!! (Video)

At the end of the last radiation treatment there was a little ceremony where I happily rang a bell that was situated right outside the door of the radiation treatment delivery room to signal the end of this part of the ordeal. I was surrounded by Melody and the wonderful technicians who helped me. They were kind and totally professional; and even went so far as to play tunes for me from my favorite musical genre—classic rock and roll—while I was being irradiated. The wan smile on my face in the pictures capturing this moment belies the discomfort from the bandaged wounds on my neck. The relief of having completed that last treatment was tremendous, but I knew that our journey through the woods of recovery was far from over.

Chapter 10: Grace with Meals

Now let's turn to grace with meals. Another one of the side effects that we were told often resulted from the chemotherapy and radiation directed to head and neck cancers was the impact on tender mouth tissue, salivary glands, and taste buds. We were told that the side effects would be worse toward the end of radiation with significant burn-like effect to the skin, but the more subtle loss

Image of Melody Zuker Preparing a Holiday Meal

of taste and dry mouth might not be fully realized until some months after the final treatments. This turned out to be unfortunately prophetic.

When we say grace with meals, the speaker often mentions taking this food for the nourishment of our bodies. My daughters Sonya and Julia remind me from time to time that during their early years at mealtime I made them say, "This food will become my body," before eating. Perhaps this was a presage of my later issues with eating and food?

But it is taken for granted that eating will also be a pleasurable experience. The food nourishes our bodies and our psyches. The entire home cooking experience of shopping for ingredients, choosing a menu (however rudimentary

Image of Melody Zuker's table set for celebration

that may be), the preparation, the actual cooking, the serving, the consuming, and the conversation that may take place concurrent with the consumption of the food prepared are all part of the drama of dining.

So often these steps are taken by rote and, in many cases, with disdain. "I hate to cook," is often heard. Or, "I never cook." And even, "The only thing I can make is a reservation," is often heard in conversation by friends and others citing a ubiquitous meme started by a comedian of the mid-1900s. I cannot remember who first said this.

Then there are those who love all the steps in the cooking and eating process. My wife Melody is one of those people. She is gifted with a talent and love of cooking. One of her greatest joys is preparing a meal that she knows will be a hit but making a few adjustments just for fun to see if they add to the experience.

What a sadness for me that Melody's gustatorial abilities have been largely lost on me as I have struggled with the loss of taste, appetite, and mouth moisture. This combination makes eating not just undesirable but downright awful.

Imagine that anything that you try to eat that is the least bit dry will turn to dust in your mouth. There is virtually no way to swallow a dry clump of bread or even dry chicken. The salivary glands are an important part of the digestive process. If they are not producing saliva normally, the entire eating experience is made frustrating and unenjoyable.

Melody pours over recipes and menu choices, appetizers, main dishes, desserts, and drinks. She makes lists of ingredients and does her shopping with a determination that is a model of single-minded focus. She returns home with her goods like the lioness returning from the savannah with kill for the pride. Then prep and cooking are done in a whirlwind.

The table-scape (for an event or holiday) must be just right with the dedicated décor for the occasion. Our garage is peppered with boxes of seasonal table decorations, place mats, napkins and serving pieces. You can certainly say that I am a lucky guy with a beautiful wife who loves to cook.

After the first round of chemotherapy, my taste was still more-or-less intact. During the hiatus between the first round and the following combination of chemotherapy and radiation, my taste came back to almost full recognition. Illustrative of that was one trip home from MD Anderson during the respite after chemotherapy and before chemo/radiation, when we stopped at a local Olive Garden for dinner. I am a big fan of the soup and salad offering with unlimited bread sticks. (Add a side of marinara sauce for dipping and it can't be beat.) I ordered the soup and salad with my usual soup choice of Pasta E Faggioli.

The first taste of the soup brought tears to my eyes. I could taste the spices in the soup, and it didn't burn my mouth.

That taste brought back memories of other dishes that were savory and comfortable. An example is Melody's cornbread dressing, which is the essence of our family Thanksgiving feast. Nothing else will do for meals of holiday celebration. Just like the Madeleines in Marcel Proust's *Remembrance of Things Past*, I was reminded powerfully of the positive sensation of food and the psychological effect of associative memory.

On this occasion, I looked around the Olive Garden dining room which was nearly at capacity and noticed so many of the diners enjoying their meals mindlessly. Now as I try to eat, I always think of the pleasure we miss by wolfing down our food. I wonder about the reaction if we could somehow temporarily turn off our sense of taste and try our food sans taste. One or two bites would be all it would take to bring our attention to our plate. And we would probably shout, "Hey, what happened to the food? I can't taste anything." And then turn the taste buds back on and see the reaction.

Suddenly the taste of the food becomes important; and eating is not just a routinized necessity that is ended with a burp and a push back from the table, desk, or fast food countertop to get to the rest of our day but a realization that we have enjoyed one of the few things in life that is predictable. Our food will satisfy us, renew us (literally because we are what we eat), and help us through the rigors of our lives. Eating is really important. Enjoying it is simply the frosting on the proverbial cake.

DYSPHAGIA – WHEN FOOD BECOMES THE ENEMY

My lack of taste, the dry mouth condition, and the soreness of my tongue all contributed to making eating a painful, unsatisfying experience. As a result, my body weight, which had begun to drop during chemotherapy, continued to fall. We met with an MDA dietician who told us about ways to deal with the weight loss and the foods that might be easier for me to swallow. She cautioned that if my weight didn't at least stabilize, then I would have to be fitted with a feeding tube. Being fed with a feeding tube is called gavage. The gastric feeding tube is called a G-tube or "button."

As the prospect of serious issues with weight loss and swallowing mounted,

I was sent to a speech-language pathologist (SLP) for swallow testing. I did a basic swallowing of different types of material, crackers and liquid, which was observed by the SLP. I also underwent a barium swallowing test where I swallowed different substances while being observed by way of an X-ray view of my swallowing process to determine if there were significant swallow difficulties or aspiration.

These tests were not difficult, but they were unpleasant because some of the stuff they asked me to eat, such as crackers, were difficult for me to swallow. I knew that I had swallowing problems and I was sure these tests would confirm that. Again, we had to wait for what we expected would be more challenges to confront.

When the tests were done, the SLP told me about my swallowing issues. I wasn't directly aspirating liquids or food while swallowing, but the epiglottis wasn't closing completely to keep food or other substances from entering the trachea. This meant that I was in greater danger of aspirating something with the attendant possible damaging effects such as pulmonary aspiration (food material or liquid entering the lungs). Anyone who has swallowed something "wrong" knows how bad that situation can be.

The SLP showed me on the barium-enhanced X-ray images where I was having a problem. My tongue had lost strength and couldn't push the food as effectively as it did before the radiation treatment. The damage to my saliva glands meant that my production of saliva was minimal. The food bolus I was trying to push was too dry to move smoothly. I was working harder than normal to move the substances.

My loss of taste meant that eating was not pleasant in any way. My favorite foods either had no taste or a bitter, non-descript taste that must have been similar to the experience of the stranded time travelers with tasteless food and drink in horror maestro Stephen King's alternate reality of the 1995 television mini-series *The Langoliers*. (This mini-series was adapted from the novella *One past Midnight* found in the anthology *Four past Midnight* by Stephen King.)

STAGE 5: BODY BREAKDOWN

Getting a G-tube installed and learning to live with it was an unhappy prospect. My weight showed no signs of stopping its drop. Our dietician discussed my continuing weight loss with our primary medical team at MDA and they decided that the time had come for me to have one of the devices implanted in my stomach.

My body had changed so much I hardly recognized it as belonging to me. This is another of those disconcerting reactions to this disease and the treatment.

The weight loss appeared to me to be mostly muscle loss in my legs, arms, and shoulders. I also noticed that my face looked drawn and tightened. All my pants began to sag on me, and shirts developed a decided droop over my shoulders. Melody noticed that in my enveloping pants I had no ass. I have never had a big booty, but with this weight loss, I had the old-man body with no butt and spindly legs. The skin on my arms and legs began to sag and bag because the muscle that had occupied the space on my frame was gone.

Along with the loss of muscle came a quite noticeable loss of strength. The resulting weakness made getting out of a low-slung chair or couch a careful, painful, deliberate action of gathering momentum and then pushing forward and upward as forcefully as possible. It took all the energy I could gather to get my weight over my knees while pushing with my weakened muscles to make the "power move" required to rise from a sitting position. Taller, firmer, straight-back chairs are much easier to manage in this weakened condition.

One of the most challenging aspects of this phase in the recovery process was sitting down and getting up from the toilet. I found that in many hotels the damned toilet is so low that sitting on the seat is hard on the knees. To compensate I found myself putting weight on my forearms and wrists while sitting down on the toilet.

This was also true of going downstairs. I would support my weight on my wrist and arms to keep the pressure off my knees that were no longer supported by strong muscles and connective tissue, making them less reliable and more painful.

This awkwardness and the resulting compensation caused me to have noticeable deterioration in my wrist joints, elbows, and shoulders. My body was simply not what it used to be. I call this part of the process "Stage 5: Body Breakdown."

After using the toilet, another one of those power moves was required to regain a standing position. In this case, my pants and underwear were around my ankles, making the process more precarious. I knew from weight-lifting that it was important to keep the head up while lifting. I found that to be true in getting up from these low-height toilets.

Getting in and out of the tub is another kind of exciting physical experience for the weakened individual.

All these movements require core strength, leg strength and good balance. All of which are limited for many post-cancer treatment persons.

Bathrooms that are designed to be accessible to those with disabilities are equipped with grip bars on the wall by the toilet, tub, and shower. This is a huge help but not always available, especially when visiting another person's home or in a hotel that doesn't have these devices available in many rooms. Insisting on an "accessible" room when making hotel reservations is a good idea.

The loss of strength can be addressed by doing resistance training which includes body weight resistance, not necessarily weights or bands. However, one of the great problems associated with this stage is that cancer recovery takes so much energy that little is left for anything else. One of the most pervasive side effects of chemotherapy and radiation is fatigue accompanied by listlessness and lack of motivation.

Walking is a terrific countermeasure to the loss of strength and stamina. But that may be challenging as well.

I tried to keep up some activity, however slight. I continued to let the dogs out, which meant I had to get my butt out of the chair and out the back door. Anything like that, getting up to refresh a drink or make a sandwich, going to the mailbox, anything that keeps you moving will help. I even tried curling the milk jug to address the sagging skin on my arms. You might say I was lactose-lifting.

There are many resources online to help, such as the exercises that one can do while sitting. These are usually directed toward arthritis sufferers, but they work for cancer recovery as well (*American Cancer Society, 2019*).

After chemotherapy and radiation, I seemed prone to injuries, aches, and pains from doing nothing. These discomforts would just suddenly appear, often in the morning as "bed injuries." Like the sore shoulders that took us to the MDA emergency room, there didn't seem to be any detectable reason for this except the changes in my body resulting from the treatment.

That reminds me of another gag by a stand-up comic who spoke about "bed injuries": When we wake up and say, "I must have slept on my [shoulder, neck, back] wrong, because it sure is sore today."

*Or the comic who said that even everyday things can hurt us. He used the
example of getting out of the bathtub and farting and sneezing at the same
time you are stepping out of the tub. He said you can possibly separate a
shoulder or break a rib doing that.*

There is another one of those activities that we take for granted. Getting in
and out of a chair is a simple matter until the body is weakened, particularly
those large muscles like the glutes, and quadriceps. I learned to tighten my
abdominal muscles and use my arms and shoulders as much as I could to
help get to my feet.

These same muscles and joints are essential in walking and standing. They
are also extremely important to maintain balance and prevent falls.

Post-treatment cancer patients should be warned specifically about the need
to compensate for the loss of muscle and the corresponding loss of strength.
This applies to core strength as well. The research into body capability continues to point with greater clarity on the importance of core strength (*University
of Kansas Cancer Center, 2019*).

I noticed that every time we came in for a follow up visit to MDA, one of
the standard questions was, "Have you fallen in the past week?" They also ask
about the most recent bowel movement. I recommend a special session on the
importance of these two aspects of cancer recovery. Failure to adjust to the
new physical reality of the post-cancer-treatment body can result in significant
problems that may put the patient in the hospital.

G-TUBE BUTTON

I had tried my best with smoothies, milkshakes, Boost, Ensure, soups, stew,
anything that we could come up with to get more calories into my body. We
were also warned against relying solely on liquid sustenance. If I did that to
the exclusion of solid food, my swallowing apparatus would atrophy; and I
would lose any ability to swallow. Keeping that admonition in mind, I would
do my best to eat solid food. Things like scrambled eggs, meat in stew or soup,
dry cereal that I let set in milk until it was soggy, and fruit like strawberries,
blueberries, and grapes. Their liquid content made it easier for them to go
down. Eating became a slower, more deliberate process for me because I had
to be very careful about putting more in my mouth than I could manage. The
old saw about biting off more than you could chew took on new meaning for
me. I had to concentrate on the chewing-and-swallowing process to be sure I

was giving my swallowing muscles the best chance for success and to avoid the dry-land-drowning sensation of misguided swallowed food or drink.

I had a constant throat-clearing action to aid in the swallowing process. I was conscious of the noise this caused and was always checking for people looking at me with either concern or disapproval as I continually cleared my throat. The SLP had shown me certain head positions while eating that helped with swallowing. The resulting eating time was longer and less was consumed. It was a pain.

The day arrived for the installation of the G-tube. This was a surgical procedure that required full anesthesia. The plug portion of the device was inserted through an incision a few inches above my naval. The device went through the skin and into the stomach. The device was an all plastic tube, and there were expanding washers inside my stomach at the point of entry and inside my skin to keep the device in place. The operation took about thirty minutes. When I woke up, there I was with this plastic tube disappearing into my stomach. In the recovery room the surgeon came in to check on my progress and to give me some information on the post-procedure regimen. They told us to expect some bleeding, but that should stop quickly.

I was given an information sheet on how to use the G-tube, how to keep it clean, how to load it with the feeding solution, and how to manage the flow of the formula into my stomach. The dietician came in and gave us some of the liquid food. It came in those plastic/cardboard type containers. It looked a little like a Boost or Muscle Milk container. We were given a case of the stuff with information on where to order more.

We were also told about a medical supply facility in Houston where we could buy one of those metal, movable IV poles. These are often seen being trundled down hospital hallways by patients on IV medication or supplementation who are required to rise from their beds and move. None of that languishing in the bed plucking the bed sheets.

Perhaps this use of the IV pole and the southern exposure of hospital gowns is best captured on film by Jack Nicholson in the 2003 rom-com *Something's Got to Give*. He perfectly captures the loopiness of the patient who has suffered a mild heart attack who is disoriented by the meds he's taking and stumbles down the hall pushing his IV pole muttering incoherently.

I thought as we loaded the device onto the back of the SUV that I was now indeed a person struggling with the aftermath of cancer treatment. I would be tethered to this mobile, metal monster for an unknown amount of time. But this pole was a hell of a lot better than trying to jury rig a place to hang the formula bag that was high enough to allow gravity to do its work but short enough to allow me to control the flow of liquid into my body by adjusting the clamps on the tube.

I was told by the dietician that I needed to ingest a minimum of 2,500 calories a day. Each of the formula containers held about 375 calories, including protein and multiple vitamins and minerals. It is a healthy combination of nutrients that goes directly into the stomach for immediate gastric processing. We were told that I would need to consume five or six cans of the formula per day depending upon how many calories I was consuming from other sources.

This regimen was designed to allow me to maintain my body weight with the ingestion of a known number of calories. The downside of course, is that there is absolutely no sensory satisfaction with this process. There is no smell, no taste, no touch of the texture and consistency of the mixture being consumed. There is also no sense of hunger.

Feeding under these conditions is a mechanical process that is done according to the clock and the need for nutrition. There is also no concomitant sense of satiety. I never felt full or satisfied after a bout with the feeding tube. I always felt like I had completed an important but unpleasant chore.

The only pleasure was one of task completion. Nothing akin to sitting down with a Big Mac and fries plus an ice-cold drink. The feeding tube was not a cheeseburger in paradise.

One factor that made my feeding situation even more difficult psychologically was watching commercial television. Almost every break in the program would contain at least one commercial about food, restaurants, fast food establishments, and food items. And they all showed consumers eating the product with absolute pleasure.

Someone like me on a dramatically restricted diet could only watch and fantasize about ordering and enjoying a Big Mac with fries and a Dr. Pepper (We are from Texas.). Or, the endless pasta servings at Olive Garden. Or, the new, improved buttermilk pancakes at Denny's or IHOP.

These commercials are designed to make the food look extra scrumptious. In fact, it rarely looks that good when served at one of these establishments. Keep in mind that I am describing fast food and chain establishments.

Melody and I love to eat out at good restaurants. However, ordering at a restaurant became a challenge for me because there were some items on the menu that I simply could not eat or—if I could manage to swallow—couldn't taste.

Overall, eating was an unenjoyable enterprise.

The dietician told us that recovering saliva production, taste, and hunger sensations would be a long, incremental process. They said it could be months before I saw any improvement, and perhaps years before eating would even come close to what it was like pre-treatment. In other words, eating would never be the same again.

Chapter 11: Radiation Treatment—Side Effects and Life Effects

When my radiation treatments began, we were told that the side effects of the treatment would be apparent before the treatment was ended. We learned that quite a few people receiving radiation were unable to complete the full number of prescribed sessions because of the effect of the treatment on the body, especially the skin.

When we arrived at MDA for radiation treatment, we went to a separate section of the hospital with its own parking garage and entry station. We were directed to one of many waiting rooms in the radiation treatment area. We were told that MDA has fifteen radiation treatment rooms that are in use five days a week from early morning to the end of the business day. There was a squadron of treatment technicians and repair personnel to keep the system and the mechanisms running smoothly. The organization of this part of the MDA operation was astounding.

We sat with our fellow radiation patients and their families and friends waiting for our time to arrive. There was a television monitor situated over the door of the treatment room with the names of all the people who had checked in for their treatment that day with the time of their appointment with the roentgens.

We often sat with the same people every time we were there. We compared notes on how many treatments we had done and how many more we had to go. We talked about the direct effect of the radiation, and the side effect symptoms that were already becoming apparent, and the steps we were taking to mitigate their impact. Some of the patients were wearing bandages around their necks for the damage the radiation had caused.

Many of the patients lived some distance from Houston and had to make living arrangements for the week of treatments. No radiation on the weekend meant some would make the long trip home for a day or so.

It was somehow comforting to be in the company of fellow sufferers who were making their way courageously through this shared ordeal. We commiserated with one another. And we celebrated together when one of us reached the last treatment and rang the bell.

I was reminded of the aphorism from Nietzsche, "That which does not kill us makes us stronger." I suppose that thought could be applied to the entire panoply of pain, anxiety, and despair that make up the totality of the cancer experience.

For those of us who are survivors, another bit of Nietzschean wisdom applies, "To live is to suffer, to survive is to find some meaning in the suffering." The meaning for many survivors of cancer is the discovery of what is truly important in life.

In fact, there are many things in life that are "important." One's work, possessions, status, and so on. But the most important thing in life is health. If health is not good, nothing is as good as it could be. But, as Nietzsche says, "Life is suffering…". But suffering when it is in the form of an illness that means life or death has a potency like no other.

The cancer question is often, not "When will I be well?" But, "What are my chances of getting well?"

The prism through which a cancer patient sees life illuminates those things that have the greatest meaning. We see the faces of our beloveds, not the inside of our office or the dashboard of our cool car. The sights of nature and the sound of music take on much greater meaning.

In my experience, I would often be overtaken with gratitude for a time when I felt no discomfort, no anxiety and wasn't thinking about anything related to cancer. I would say to myself, "I haven't thought about cancer in an hour, an afternoon, a day!" I don't think I ever came close to making it cancer-thought-free for more than a day.

Chapter 12: Family and Friends

SONYA'S STORY

Every life is replete with happiness, sadness, success, and failure. There are also, occasionally, the coincidences that seem so striking that they appear to be enabled by a powerful force unknown to us. This happened in the course of my cancer diagnosis and treatment.

My oldest daughter Sonya, who was adopted during my first marriage in 1975 at the age of three from Vietnam, was diagnosed with colon cancer about three months after I was diagnosed with mine.

This coincidence was made more implausible by the fact that colon cancers usually affect older people. Sonya has always been a fit person and did not seem to be a good candidate for cancer.

One thing we do not know was any presence of cancer in her biological family. She had been left at the orphanage when she was an infant, and we had no knowledge of her parents. We knew that her biological father was Caucasian and her mother was probably Vietnamese.

My first wife and I decided to adopt after it became clear that we could not have biological children of our own. We decided that we would try to adopt a mixed-race, female child from Vietnam knowing the difficulties faced by those children, especially the girls.

In many cases, we learned, a mixed-blood, female baby in Vietnam would simply be put outdoors to die. This probably most often happened in the jungle villages where another female child was not seen as a valuable working member of the family but simply another drain on scarce resources. Female, mixed-blood children born in the cities could easily find themselves sold into the sex-for-hire underworld.

We had assistance with this effort from a wealthy Vietnamese family that I met through my work at Duke University. Once they heard of our desire to adopt one of these children, they offered to help us work through the byzantine adoptions system in place at that time in war-torn Vietnam. Matters were made more complex and urgent because by the time we decided to try to do this, the future existence of the corrupt regime that we had supported in Saigon had no chance to survive against the North Vietnamese once we had pulled out of the country. Our friends in Vietnam found three little girls in an orphanage in Saigon managed by Buddhist and Catholic nuns that were the right age, around two or three years, that we hoped to adopt. I remember the three pictures vividly. Only one of the little girls appeared to be mixed-race, Asian and Caucasian. We chose her and sent word back to Saigon to proceed with all possible haste to get the paperwork required at the US Embassy.

By this time in 1975, the situation in Saigon was chaotic. The Vietnamese who had worked with the American Armed Forces were trying desperately to escape Saigon before the North Vietnamese Army captured the city. The South Vietnamese forces were in full retreat. Some were even leaving their uniforms and weapons in the street and melting into the city to avoid capture as a prisoner of war.

We learned from our friends that there were difficulties with Sonya's (We had already decided on her name.) paperwork and they were unable to get her visa for entry into the US.

We were frantic because we knew the noose around the neck of Saigon was tightening, and it was only a matter of days or hours before the city fell.

You may remember the heartbreaking pictures of the helicopters on the roof of the US Embassy and the GIs fighting off the desperate Vietnamese trying to force their way into the choppers. It was a waking nightmare for us knowing that our little girl was caught in this disaster. We thought there was little chance she would be able to get out.

Then there was the disaster of the Operation Babylift flight which crashed shortly after takeoff with many Vietnamese children on board being evacuated to adoptive homes. Seventy-eight children on that flight were killed along with fifty adults. We had no idea if she was on that flight (*Martin & NPR Staff, 2015*).

We had no word from our friends during those final days of the American withdrawal from Saigon. The city fell on April 30, 1975. A few days after the fall, some of the family of our friends in Vietnam who were living near us received a telegram saying that their family had escaped from Saigon and were now on Guam waiting for transport to the U.S. No mention was made of Sonya's fate. A few days later, after frantic telegrams to Guam, we received another telegram telling us that Sonya was with them on Guam and that she was safe. We wept with relief.

A few days more passed, and we heard that the family and Sonya had been airlifted to Fort Chaffee, Arkansas, which is located near Fort Smith, Arkansas, for processing into the U.S. My wife and I immediately made plans to travel to Fort Smith and try to bring Sonya back with us to Durham, North Carolina.

I contacted a representative of the Catholic Relief organization who was working at Fort Chaffee with the refugees. I asked him if he could try to find our little girl among the thousands of refugees that had poured into the camp. The next day he called back to tell us he had found her. He said, "She is beautiful."

We arrived at Fort Smith and rented a car which we drove to Fort Chaffee. We arrived there at dusk, and the sight was amazing. There were Vietnamese refugees everywhere.

They had been assigned to WWII-era barracks. There were bulletin boards set up with hundreds of pictures of loved ones that were lost to the refugees who were there but that might have been somewhere in that throng of lost souls. Food lines had been set up; sanitation stations and telephone banks were available for those with relatives or friends already in the States. I saw one young woman throwing up on the side of the road as we walked toward the building where we were told that the family with Sonya was located.

I could only imagine the level of stress that these people must have been feeling having fled their homes and traveling thousands of miles to land in this starkly unfamiliar location. I was amazed at how quickly the US authorities had been able to mobilize the resources needed to set up this camp and welcome these disconnected thousands.

Looking back on what I saw on that trip, I must wonder why we can't do the same thing on our southern border to administer to those asylum seekers in far fewer numbers than the wave of immigrant/asylum seekers coming from Southeast Asia?

We arrived at the building and met the family who had been helping us in Saigon.

It was easy to identify me and my wife since I was the only Caucasian in sight, standing 6'3", weighing around 230 pounds, sporting a rather bushy mustache.

Sonya was nowhere in sight. She was with one of the girls in the family we knew. Suddenly, she appeared; and she was beautiful. She appeared Eurasian but her hair was curly and lighter in color than the other children.

My first wife, who is full-blooded Korean, stepped toward her and put her arms around her. She turned to me and pointed and told Sonya, "There is your new daddy."

I doubt that Sonya understood many of those words, but she took one look at me head-to-toe, went, "Yipe," and ran for the door. I don't think she had ever been as close to someone who looked like me before.

We collected Sonya to take her back to our motel. As soon as she got into the car, she fell into a deep sleep and began to sweat profusely. We stopped at KFC (Kentucky Fried Chicken) first and carried her into our room when we arrived. She woke up to eat and then went right back into the deep sleep with sweating. She must have been exhausted from the travel and the stress of the past days of travail and travel.

The next day we went back to Fort Chaffee and checked her out of the processing center. We said goodbye to our helpful family because they had to stay and finish their out-processing.

When we got off the airplane in Durham, the press corps from the city was there to greet us. They had heard that we were adopting one of the Vietnamese orphans and bringing her home from Arkansas. Sonya was front page news in the *Durham Sun* for a couple of days.

Sonya's adjustment to life in Durham was relatively easy considering her background. She picked up English almost overnight. When she arrived, she spoke Vietnamese. She also understood and spoke a little French because Vietnam had been a French colony from 1862 until 1954, and the capital Saigon, often referred to as the "Paris of the Far East," had an especially strong French influence.

We did make a mistake of taking her to a 4th of July fireworks celebration at the Duke University football stadium. When the first loud explosive fireworks were detonated, Sonya hit the deck at our feet. She was shaking and obviously frightened. We scooped her up and headed for home. It dawned on us that during the final days of the siege of Saigon there must have been a lot of artillery shelling and bombing that would have been brought back to her by the sounds of the fireworks (Isaacs & Downing, 1998).

Our family expanded again when we adopted a three-month old baby, a full-blooded Korean whom we named Julie. Julie was our sweet baby and rapidly grew into a bright, bouncing toddler. When we took the girls to the mall, we were often stopped by people who would point at Sonya and say, "You look just like your daddy." (One Caucasian and the other half Caucasian.) Then they would point to Julie and say, "And you look just like your mommy" (both full-blooded Koreans).

Over the years, Sonya grew to be a tall, willowy, accomplished young woman. She excelled at ballet and had an excellent high school record. She began college at the University of California Santa Cruz and completed her bachelor's degree at the University of Redlands in southern California.

Sonya's mother and I divorced in 1996. At that time, Sonya and I drifted apart. She married and moved to Minnesota with her husband. They had two children, Mitchell and Emma.

Another aspect of the coincidence of Sonya's cancer with mine was that it was only a year before her diagnosis in 2014 that she and I had a reconciliation, meeting at her home in White Bear Lake, Minnesota. It was then that I met her children (my grandchildren) for the first time. By this time Sonya was divorced, working full-time, and being the single parent. She was determined to be the best mother possible and do all she could for her two children. I loved being with them and having the chance for them to get to know their heretofore unknown grandfather.

When Sonya notified Melody and me (Melody and I married in November 2000.) of her diagnosis, I thought, *This can't be happening. Both of us diagnosed with cancer at the same time.* It didn't seem fair, but then nothing about cancer is fair.

Colorectal cancer is relatively rare for people under 50 years of age, but the rate of cancer in younger people is rising. Sonya was 42 at the time she was diagnosed. The average age at the time of diagnosis for women is 72 (American Cancer Society, 2019).

Sonya's doctors told her that the treatment plan for her would be chemotherapy followed by surgery to remove the cancerous section of her colon. Typical of Sonya, she approached this news with determination. She was going to do all that she could to make the best of the situation for her and her children.

Sonya and I went through the cancer treatment regimen at almost the same time. Sonya was diagnosed a couple of months after mine was discovered. But the treatment schedule was almost the same. Sonya did not have radiation, but she had chemotherapy and surgery. I had no surgery but endured the radiation.

We kept each other informed about our procedures and their outcomes when the information became available. We compared symptoms and side-effects. We both suffered from peripheral neuropathy after chemotherapy. Because of the effect of radiation on my tasting and swallowing, I lost weight. Sonya's weight stayed about the same at first, but then she gained weight. That may have been the effect of the medication, including some doses of steroids.

Like me, Sonya had a lot of support from her co-workers and friends in Minnesota. Emma and Mitchell and her partner Tim were by her side through the entire process. I had Melody with me in Dallas. We both had support of other family living hundreds of miles away, but close emotionally. And we had each other.

One of the greatest joys in my survivorship time has been the renewed relationship with Sonya and the love found with her and her beautiful children. Sonya and I share the fact that we are survivors not only of the cancers that we both faced but also of the estrangement that had darkened our lives.

The lesson for me in this is to never give up on a relationship that was once beautiful and meaningful. If there is any hope left in such a situation, keep it alive and nurture it in the hope that it will once again flourish. We can never know what lies ahead for us in our short time on earth. Staying positive through all the turns and surprises allows us to be flexible and resourceful when we most need our friends and loved ones, and they most need us to accept the support they offer.

A LOT OF HELP FROM FRIENDS AND FAMILY

The positive effect of the support network for a cancer patient cannot be overstated. I hope I have already made it clear how much Melody's ministrations have meant to me in this cancer journey, from my first inkling that something was wrong until the present day. The statement that "I couldn't have made it without her" is precisely true and continues to apply to my current state of survivorship. Additionally, we had great support from family members and friends who were aware of my condition.

It occurred to me that the question of who to tell about one's cancer can be a bit of a problem. During the height of the side effect onslaught, it was easy to tell that I wasn't alright. I had lost my hair and about thirty pounds of body weight. A lot of people who hadn't seen me since before the cancer onset didn't recognize me. I had no issues with telling people, but I always tried to do so in a matter of fact manner without elaboration.

People often wanted to know, "What type of cancer do you have?" When I told them that I had a squamous cell carcinoma at the base of my tongue, there was usually an eye widening of the conversant because I expect they thought they would hear, prostate, lung, colon, or one of the other more widespread cancer types.

Head and neck cancers are relatively rare. It was 3.9% of the incidence of invasive cancers among men in 2016 (*CDC, 2018*). I was a little self-conscious that some people had heard that this type of cancer was caused by oral sex. You may recall that in 2013 Michael Douglas publicly announced that his cancer of the tongue was caused by human papillomavirus (HPV), which is a common sexually transmitted virus and was transmitted in his case by oral sex, cunnilingus (CDC).

I am reminded of that scene in the classic 1983 film *Terms of Endearment*. The Debra Winger character Emma has been diagnosed with cancer. Her best friend Patsy doesn't know how to deal with the cancer. The subject is avoided at a luncheon with her cool friends. Emma tells her it is okay to talk about cancer. Later at a party given by Patsy, a woman seeks out Emma and says, "Patsy tells me you have cancer." Patsy is nearby and overhears this exchange and nearly chokes on her crudité.

I daresay that most cancer sufferers have had at least one such moment. My recommendation to cancer patients is be prepared for such comments and calibrate your response to be even-handed and open. The questioner is probably uncomfortable with the topic unless they are also a cancer-experienced person. In that case, such persons often want to tell you their cancer story or the story of their parent or friend who has/had cancer. Accept the interest with grace and make the teller feel good. After all, you are still there to make a comment. That is good.

During my treatment, our daughters Natalie and Ashley, who were living in Dallas (Another reason Melody was excited at the prospect of being in Dallas), and our daughter Julia, who lives in Claremont, California, with her family made trips to Houston to help us with our treatment regimen. Their presence and concern were a great comfort to both of us.

Melody's family was also supportive. Melody's sister Tracy, who lived near Houston with her family, also visited and helped us. Melody's sister Sallie was also very supportive. Melody's wonderful father Bill and I talked on the phone repeatedly. We also made trips to visit Bill. He always made me feel better about my condition. I will never forget his kindness and love.

Our friends Debbie and Ralph from Austin and Renea and Richard from

Houston made trips to see us and lend their support. Ralph made it a point to call and give me a boost when he knew I had been through a rough patch.

Melody's coworkers at Alvin High School near Houston took up a collection and presented it to Melody, saying that they knew that cancer treatment stresses the family with unexpected costs.

Our insurance is excellent, but their kindness touched our hearts and certainly helped us with our out-of-pocket costs.

I was in the Alpha Tau Omega fraternity during my undergraduate years at Duke. I was active in the fraternity as vice president, scholarship officer, and song leader. The song leadership assignment became the stuff of legend with my classmates. Not that I was a great singer. I'm not. But I did lead the brothers at our parties and some other occasional events in such ATO classics as the "Sweetheart Song."

Once the word went out that I had cancer, I received phone calls and emails from many of my ATO brothers. It is difficult to find the words to express how much those communications from the comrades of my youth meant to me. Several have stayed in touch over the years since my treatment. At one of our reunions a couple of years ago, I had the chance to thank in person many of those supporters who were there. I publicly told them how much Melody and I benefited during those dark days from their expressions of concern and love.

I am the oldest of four boys. Interestingly, Melody is the oldest of four girls. After we met, we compared notes on being the oldest and the benefits and liabilities of such birth-order influences. My younger brothers Ron, the second son, and Michael, the youngest, and their wives Lana and Tina, respectively, stayed in constant contact with us through the treatment. Unfortunately, Murray, the third son, passed away during the time of my cancer and treatment. My brothers and I have never been especially close. But we always stayed near at hand, especially when circumstances would call the family together for good times and bad.

During the toughest time of my treatment, we were helped with several house repair and upgrade projects by our friend Hermilo. Hermilo was not only an excellent contractor, worker, and job manager, he was a constantly sympathetic person to me and Melody. He played an especially important role in helping us prepare our home for sale.

Every time we talked, whether by phone or in person on the job, he expressed real concern for my well-being. He suggested Mexican remedies for some of my conditions. He brought some of the remedies to the house for me to try. We met Hermilo's family and immediately felt their good wishes as well. Since our move to Dallas, we have missed Hermilo's expertise and positive vibe. We continue to wish him and his family the best. We give thanks that he was there to help us through tough times.

I strongly encourage anyone who learns that a friend or loved one has cancer to contact them and let them know that you are sending good wishes to them and their caregivers. That's all you need to say. That simple expression of care will lift the darkness a little.

DEATH IN THE FAMILY

During this challenging time, we had stark reminders that life goes on despite the incursion of cancer into everything we did. Our family suffered the loss of two important members—my younger brother Murray and Melody's dad Bill. Either of these losses would have been devastating, but coming on the heels of cancer for me and Sonya and occurring just one week apart made it even more debilitating.

Murray's death was difficult because of the unusual circumstances. Murray had always been somewhat eccentric. He never married and kept five cats in the house where he lived alone except for his cat companions. He became reclusive and rarely had any of us visit him.

I only recall one time that I went to his home. At one point I told Murray that if he added one more cat, he would become the weird cat guy down the street.

He died at home alone, and his body was not discovered until a week had passed. His body had decomposed to the point that the coroner could not determine a cause of death. Making it even more difficult was that when we entered his house, we found that he had become a hoarder. His house was full of newspapers, books, DVDs, and all manner of other stuff stacked and jammed into every room and corner.

Melody's dad Bill was a remarkable man. He served in the Pacific during WWII. After the war, he was a Big Band musician in east Texas and performed all over the ArkLaTex (Arkansas, Louisiana, Texas) region. He played several instruments, but the clarinet was his favorite. He made a name for himself and his music in the post-war heyday of the Big Band sound that remained his favorite throughout his life. He attended the University of Texas and after graduation, became a band director in high schools in Texas.

Bill met Beatrice, an East Texas beauty, Baylor graduate, and schoolteacher. They married and their first born was a girl they named Melody in honor of Bill's love of music. As a toddler, Melody became the mascot of one of Bill's school bands and famously rode atop one of the big bass drums when the band took the field. Melody went on to become a twirler and drum major in her own middle and high school bands.

Soon after meeting Melody's parents, I knew they were both special. But I soon fell in love with Bill. His sense of humor, intelligence, and joy of living were infectious. His passing hit both of us hard. Melody's mother passed in 2009, and Bill had lived alone after that near one of Melody's sisters. We made regular trips to visit Bill in Kerrville, Texas. He had been struggling with some health issues but continued to enjoy his friends near his home and the weekly events at the Elks Club. He attended the dances and was sought after as a dance partner by his many female admirers. Bill once said, "I may have trouble walking, but I can still dance."

As Bill aged, he became philosophical about the ways in which age was experienced. He hated not being as active as he once was. He didn't like being alone and loved our visits, the visits of others, and the camaraderie of his crew in Kerrville. He once told us that, "The days do drag on, but the years—they fly by." I don't know if he picked up that aphorism somewhere along the line, but he observed the phenomenon in his own life winsomely. It didn't trouble him particularly because he always had that twinkle in his eye up to his last days.

During our visits, Bill and I would often sit and listen to some of the Big Band tunes from his extensive collection of the Big Band icons. I knew something about the Big Band era because my parents loved it. "Their song" was "Paper Doll" by the Mills Brothers, released in 1943. I was proud to tell Bill that one of the greats from that era, Les Brown of *Les Brown and his Band of Renown*, attended my alma mater Duke University, where he led the band under the name *Les Brown and His Blue Devils*.

Bill always enjoyed a good laugh. I have been known to tell stories and jokes. (Just ask Melody and she will tell you that I often tell the same joke repeatedly. What the heck? If it's a good story, it is worth retelling. Bill enjoyed my attempts at humor.)

We were talking about his friends at the Elks Club one day when I told him this one about…

(T)he two older guys sitting at the bar. One turned to the other and said. "You know I just read that during mating season Elks have sex six or seven times a day." The other, older gentleman puts down his beer and says, "Darn, and I just joined the Moose Club."

Bill laughed out loud. It was one of my great pleasures to get a smile or an outright guffaw out of Bill at the retelling of one of my jokes.

WHAT I LEARNED FROM 2014

Bill and Murray died within days of each other in 2014 while we were going through my treatment process. Melody and I said more than once that 2014 had not been a great year considering there had been two cancers and two deaths in the family. We were happy to see the arrival of 2015 and put the old year away.

The realization of how little we knew of Murray's life was upsetting to me and my surviving brothers. We took some comfort in that it appeared his death was without distress. It was hard not to fall back into one of the earlier stages of cancer awareness and acceptance—Why is this happening to us? I recognized something years ago that my father presaged as he grew older, that life always presents us with the drama of things coming to an end—youth, the childhood of our children, the lives of our parents, jobs, the lives of friends and other loved ones, the way one looks, strength, vitality, and enjoyment of certain things.

As Dad's friends began to pass, my father became increasingly despondent. I think he felt left behind. He began to suffer some of the unavoidable consequences of old age and his despondency became increasingly bitter. His enjoyment of life was dramatically foreshortened. This affected my mother and her life as well.

My learning from this was a revisiting of one of my early heroes in the study of psychology and philosophy, Viktor Frankl. I read *Man's Search for Meaning* (which was originally titled *From Death Camp to Existentialism*) many years ago and was profoundly touched by Frankl's recounting of his experiences in the Nazi death camps and how he managed to find some meaning even in the most extreme conditions ever visited upon a people. I was affected by the quote below.

The one thing you can't take away from me is the way I choose to respond to what you do to me.

The last of one's freedoms is to choose one's attitude in any given circumstance, to choose one's own way."

(Viktor Frankl in *Man's Search for Meaning,* 1946)

Another quote that affected me greatly was by Kipling when he spoke of Triumph and Disaster and seemed to say that Life will take its toll at the same time it is giving us unbelievable rewards.

If you can meet with Triumph and Disaster And treat those two impostors just the same;

(Rudyard Kipling in the poem *"If,"* 1895)

Chapter 13: As Life Goes On

MORE ON SIDE EFFECTS

After the first round of chemotherapy was completed, I noticed that my hands and feet began to tingle. My hands also became much more sensitive to the cold. I couldn't hold a cold can of beer or soda without a lot of discomfort.

My doctors told us this was peripheral neuropathy and was a likely side effect of the chemotherapy. I thought the word peripheral in the term referred to the location of the condition in the hands and feet. But in reference to nerves, it means there is damage done to nerves outside the spinal-cord and brain (*mayoclinic.org, 2019*).

The doctors prescribed gabapentin (brand name Neurontin), a drug which is widely used to treat nerve-related conditions. I had previously been prescribed gabapentin when I had shingles, another nerve-involved ailment that is no fun. Fortunately, there are vaccines that prevent the onset of shingles. They are worth every penny if they allow one to avoid the pain of shingles.

The drug has significant side effects. The most often noted is sleepiness, dizziness, and tiredness (*Cunha, 2018*). I have been on the drug for years now and have not noticed the side effects causing significant problems for me. The drug may mitigate the peripheral neuropathy's worst symptoms, but the tingling and cold sensitivity continue and have now become part of my post-cancer-treatment life.

WORKING WITH CANCER

Work was certainly not the most important thing in my life, but it was a crucial part of my self-identity. I have had the good fortune of working in higher education my entire professional career. I have worked at eight excellent institutions over the forty-six years of my career, all of them populated with terrific people, students, faculty, staff, and alumni.

When I was diagnosed with cancer in 2014, I was working at Texas Chiropractic College (TCC), located near Houston, Texas. I was hired in 2009 as Dean of Enrollment. Then I became the Vice President of Enrollment and was named the Interim President in 2013. It was during this last assignment that I was diagnosed.

One of my closest colleagues, Dr. Clay McDonald, who had been my supervisor, had already left TCC for the presidency at Logan University in St. Louis, MO. He and I stayed in close contact, and he and his wife Terry were a constant source of support to Melody and me. They made the trip to Houston to visit with us during some of the toughest days of the side-effects assault. Their kindness was much appreciated.

The outgoing president of TCC and the Board of Trustees were very supportive as we began the treatment and throughout the entire time until I left TCC in September 2014. One of the senior members of the Board told me not to worry about the job but to do all I needed to do to protect my health. I did what I could for as long as I could for the college until the effects made it impossible for me to carry on. Even then I was on the college roster until the time I left TCC. The kindness of all my friends at TCC made the ordeal much easier for us to bear.

That same outgoing president gave me some words of wisdom when I hit the 65-year mark and became eligible for Medicare. He told me to be sure and shop for the best possible Medicare supplement we could afford. This was years before the cancer appeared.

I thought about what he had said and decided to do some research and settled on a supplemental insurance package that seemed to be first rate. All the reviews were positive, and we signed on concurrent with the Medicare start.

It turned out to be one of the best investments we ever made. The supplement filled the gap left by the basic Medicare coverage. It also made me a more attractive patient to the providers that decided if they would take on new Medicare patients.

I strongly encourage anyone approaching Medicare membership to evaluate what they think they will need to supplement their Medicare benefits depending upon their personal situation of health and other resources that might be available. There are plenty of providers out there happy to sell you the additional coverage they provide. Be a good consumer and check the reviews and discuss with others who are already enrolled to see about their experience with various providers.

The time it takes to find the right plan could be a very important part of future financial solvency in the unfortunate event of catastrophic illness or injury. One great advantage is reducing the anxiety that comes with the astronomical cost of cancer treatment. The cost of drugs alone can be ruinous.

My staff and faculty colleagues were great supporters. The students, my students, were most understanding. I taught clinical psychology at TCC for four years. One of my colleagues volunteered to help me with my teaching duties as the treatment became more burdensome. This was especially important since the role of interim president required me to be away from campus quite often.

During virtually all my tenure at the various institutions where I worked, I was able to teach. I taught, humanistic psychology, abnormal psychology, clinical psychology, and the psychology of adolescence.

The time I spent teaching was some of the most meaningful of my career. It is difficult to describe the feeling one gets in the classroom when you see that your students are "getting it." They are with you and not checking email on their laptops. That experience is unforgettable.

Before I completed my Ph.D. in counseling psychology, I taught self-defense for the Physical Education Departments at the two earliest institutions where I worked. That teaching assignment was made possible in part by my study of Tae Kwon Do, which I began practicing during my deployment to Korea during my US Army service from 1968 to 1971. (A memoir of my Army experience titled *Standing Tall and Looking Good: One Soldier's Life and Lessons Learned from 1968 to 1971* was published on *Amazon and is available in paperback and Kindle eBooks.*)

I continued to work at TCC for as long as I could and then realized that I was not being effective. My duties as interim president had been given to a member of the Board who had long experience in the chiropractic profession and was a graduate of the college. My teaching duties were assumed by my colleague and plans were made by my faculty supervisor to find a permanent replacement until the time that I could return to full time.

It was during the treatment phase that I received a call from the president of Parker University in Dallas Dr. Brian McAulay. Brian and I had become friends at various meetings of the chiropractic educational leadership. Brian was a long-time member of this group and well respected by all his contemporaries. He asked me if I might be interested in coming to work for him as Assistant to the President. He knew of my work at TCC and my many years in various positions in higher education.

When I told Melody of this, she was listening carefully. In fact, she said that she could be ready to move to Dallas the next day. Melody is from east Texas, where Dallas is considered the Texas equivalent of Mecca.

I told Brian about my cancer treatment and that some time would probably have to pass before I would be in any shape to make a move to a new location and a new job. Brian told me that he was happy to wait until I felt I was ready for the change. I told him that his willingness to wait was much appreciated.

We asked my doctors at MDA how long they thought my recovery would be before I had the strength to make changes like the ones we were contemplating. They said that it would depend upon how I reacted to the side effects that they knew would continue to peak for a while before I saw any real improvement. In other words, it would be up to me to do all I could to regain my strength and adjust to my post-cancer-treatment body and psyche. Much of this depended upon my success in gaining weight. The feeding tube was part of my routine, but eating solid food continued to be a challenge.

My weight stabilized but stubbornly refused to budge upward. I still looked gaunt and tired, but I was beginning to feel better overall. Melody noted that all my clothes were swallowing me, especially pants. I had lost so much weight in my legs and butt that the pants billowed round my bottom making me look more like Charlie Chaplain than myself. We invested in clothes that were closer to my new frame. Wearing them made me feel better and less like a person I didn't recognize.

When I was a football player at Duke University, I stood about 6'3" plus and weighed around 230 pounds. I was a denizen of the weight room and pushed hard to improve my strength and body weight for football.

Before the onset of the cancer, I had dropped in weight to about 210 pounds and had lost about an inch in height as I began to experience disc compression in my spine resulting in sciatica and other issues related to nerve impingement. I developed a drop foot situation where my foot would flop as I walked and I had lost strength and tone in my anterior tibialis, the muscle on the outside front of the shin that raises the foot when activated. These were the first symptoms I had that were real-life reminders that advancing age and the cumulative effect of all my athletic endeavors were having on my body. I would tell people that my body is now cashing the checks that I had written fifty years before.

The last radiation treatment was in late July. As we looked at the calendar, I felt the presence of the feeding tube attached to my stomach and knew that my weight was a long way from the threshold needed to get off the tube. I wondered aloud, "How can I work with this damned tube sticking out of my stomach and me limited to very specific types of food?" I was also weakened with the loss of weight. I was never immobilized, or bed ridden, but I didn't have much stamina.

We settled on a target date for me to start at Parker University at the end of September 2014. Melody was skeptical that I could be ready that soon. I really didn't know either, but I did know that this was an opportunity that I did not want to miss. And I wanted to start as soon as possible given my straitened circumstances. I hoped that the structure of the job would help me recover physically and mentally.

I began to feel better and stronger as I mastered the stomach tube regimen. I tried to eat solid food as much as I could. Anything dry was still a major challenge, even with liquid to wash it down.

We put our house in Houston on the market, and within twenty-four hours we had offers more than our asking price. The market was extremely hot for sellers at that time in Houston. We lived in Clear Lake, a neighborhood near the Johnson Space Center where many NASA professionals lived. It was a desirable place to live, within easy driving distance of downtown Houston and with a culture all its own. The Clear Lake campus of the University of Houston was a plus, as well as proximity to the Kemah Boardwalk with all the waterfront amenities of a resort destination.

A MOVING EXPERIENCE

Melody and I have moved many times in the course of our marriage, and every time we are reminded of what a travail it is to go through all the stages of moving—decision to move, putting the house on the market, finding other accommodations in the moving destination, gathering boxes for packing, packing, loading, driving, storage, unloading, unpacking, more unpacking, and swearing to never buy any more books that aren't absolutely essential. All of this had to be managed without relying too much on alcohol or other self-medication to get it done.

Melody was the major force behind the move and found a nice place for us to land in Dallas upon our first arrival. It was a high-rise apartment building in uptown Dallas in a popular area that featured several blocks of restaurants and bars. It attracted a high energy, younger crowd that seemed to lean on their auto horns every night starting at about 11:00 o'clock. We always wondered what the hell they were honking about.

We were on the seventh floor with our two little Yorkies Abbey and Lucy, who were not used to upper floor living. Yorkies are notorious for their tiny bladders. They only weighed five and four pounds, respectively. This meant we had to hook them to their leashes and take the elevator down seven flights to the garage basement and then outside to do their business. Those were long trips, but necessary. They tried their best to be good girls, but we did invest heavily in puppy pads for the apartment.

We didn't stay long in the apartment building. The traffic challenge for me to get from this crowded, uptown location to the Parker campus was draining. Also, it was simply too difficult for us to manage the up and down requirements of the seventh-floor location. It was clear that we were in a location populated by millennials working in the rough-and- tumble world of upwardly mobile Dallas. I think we raised the median age of the residents of our building by at least a few years when we moved in.

Our next location was a town house located near the busy intersection of Lovers Lane and Greenville Avenue in north Dallas. That was the area of Dallas where we wanted to live, and it was closer to my job at Parker University. It was a nice townhouse community. Our place was great except that there was a long stairway to the upstairs living area. This meant a challenge for me with my worn-out knees and the puppies needing their outdoor time.

Luckily, the location was good for house hunting and visiting potential locations. Melody went at finding a house with determination, knowing that the sooner we were settled the better for everyone.

Melody found several homes that were in our price range and in neighborhoods that we thought would be a good fit for us. Two of her first finds turned out to be compromised by the shifting soils that are well known in north Texas. The houses in this area are largely built on concrete slabs. When the soil shifts, the slabs will often crack after subsidence. This results in windows and door frames cracking and becoming ill-fitting. Plumbing built into the slab may also be compromised, resulting in gradual leakage with damage to foundation and flooring.

We were losing hope until Melody found a home located in the Lake Highlands area of north Dallas. I knew this area well since it is near White Rock Lake, which is a training area for many of the runners in Dallas. It is also incorporated into the White Rock Marathon racecourse, which is now the Dallas Marathon.

I ran "the Rock", as we called it then, in 1996. It was a great race, but the day turned quite hot despite the early December date. Several hours after the race, I found myself in a local hospital ER, hooked up to a bag of saline solution to counter dehydration. I was soon back on my feet no worse for the wear of 26.2 miles of north Dallas scenery.

The house was built circa 1963 but had been remodeled with a more open floor plan, five bedrooms, and three bathrooms. It was built on pier and beam which was much less susceptible to the damage inflicted by the inescapable disruption of soil movement. We made an offer, and it was accepted. Hurray! We had a home.

Now we just had to move for the third time in less than five months. At least, this would only be another across town move and from a storage facility to the new (to us) house. This move was to be our last move if we had anything to do with that decision.

These moving experiences made me philosophical about the moving process. I made notes of several things to remember that help in a move:

1. Anticipate moving as far in advance as possible.
2. Evaluate how this move will affect you financially.
    a. Will you be reimbursed for moving expenses if it is for a job?
    b. You will need accurate records of all moving expenses for reimbursement or tax purposes.
3. If you own your home, do an evaluation of what you must do to prepare your home for sale.
4. Start making lists of "things to do right away"
    a. Find a realtor (if possible, go online and start searching);
    b. Begin to locate a mover;
    c. Do the self-study of how much your move will cost (There are online questionnaires about number of rooms, large items, pianos, pool tables, etc.).
5. Make a file folder and put ALL the pertinent documents in that folder. Make copies of emails and put them in the folder.
6. Make a list of phone numbers and email addresses of all the people you need—realtor, mover, handy man, loan officer, financial persons, plumbers, roofers, and others.

Because of my weakened condition, I was assigned to do most of the research on finding the people we needed to help us make the move. I sought out moving companies, read their reviews, and completed their questionnaires to get an estimate on how much the move would cost us. My new employer was going to help with some of the moving expenses, but there was a limit on the amount.

Image of employee ID card for Zuker when he worked at Parker University

I worked with Hermilo on the repairs we needed to make to satisfy our buyers. I also communicated with all the entities that needed notifying that we were moving—utility companies, neighbors, members of the family who may not have gotten the word about the cancer, the new job, and the move.

All of this will take time, and you will need to know what your time horizon is for selling your house. If necessary, you will be coordinating with anyone working for you, your spouse, and children. You will be dealing with issues such as day care, schools, transportation, and how to go about commutes to and from your workplace(s). If you are going to a new job, you must factor in the time it will take to get accustomed to the new demands.

STARTING A NEW JOB

Going through cancer-treatment side effects, I really had no idea what level of difficulty the new job would entail. The job description was essentially to relieve the president of some of his duties, such as writing memos and welcoming visitors to the campus. I was his utility man without portfolio. I had a lot of experience with all of these activities. It was more a matter of finding out how much I could do to make this job effective for my boss.

I was worried that my wasted appearance might be a negative factor for me and my new colleagues. I look at the ID photo that was taken of me soon after I arrived at Parker, and I shudder when I see my drawn countenance, wan smile, and stubby white hair that had begun to grow back on my bald pate.

But, I thought, *This is what I've got, and they will either take it or I will leave it.* Having worked in higher education for over forty years, I fully expected my colleagues to give me the benefit of their hopes for my success.

The job I was assigned had a good deal of latitude between me and my boss, the president. I was assigned to give him some assistance with his more mundane duties that would free him for the bigger-picture demands of his office, including the many off-campus meetings and travel that were a natural order for a college president. I could even stand in for him in certain settings, having done the ceremonial pieces of the presidency at two institutions before. I knew I could help because I had been to these rodeos many times and my chemo-brain fog had largely dissipated as the days since I rang that bell at the MDA radiation treatment facility had accrued.

I reported to Parker University on September 29, 2014. Angela Klement, the Executive Assistant to the President, showed me to my new digs and told me that she would take care of anything that I needed for the office and would help with all the accoutrement of the job, cell phone, ID card, business cards, and so on. I was scheduled for my Human Resources orientation meeting and prepared myself mentally and physically to get to work. Damn it felt good to be a worker.

ARE YOU WORKING HARD OR HARDLY WORKING?

When I started the job at Parker University, I was in my forty-second year in higher education. I had been doing these jobs since 1971, right after my separation from the Army. I have loved all my jobs, some more than others. But all have been challenging and rewarding.

Colleges and universities are great places to work. They are usually quite beautiful. Campuses are designed to create a learning and living environment that is welcoming and sheltered. They are populated with many smart people. The students are (usually) eager learners and happy to be there.

But these bucolic settings and earnest, educated people belie the fact that colleges and universities, just like any organization, are often riddled with jealousy, frustration, disappointment, backstabbing, in-fighting, treachery, and dissembling. In other words, colleges and universities are just like any organization.

Supervisors can be authoritarian, demanding, demeaning, and destructive. In my case, I have worked for and with some of the best people I have ever known. There have been a few that, for many reasons, were not the best people for me or the organization. I'm sure there are some people that I have worked with over the years that would say the same about me.

The leaders at Parker were wonderfully supportive and determined to make a positive difference in the lives of the faculty and staff, and most importantly, in the lives of the students. I started as Assistant to the President, a man I knew well and for whom I had deep admiration and respect. We worked well together, and I think I was able to help him in areas where he needed assistance to meet the demands of the president's unending schedule and political pressures.

After a few weeks, I began to feel at home with my new surroundings and the people in my circle. I was a member of the President's Cabinet. We had weekly meetings and, soon after my arrival, a three-day retreat off campus to plan for the coming academic year.

I had already had five years of experience in the world of chiropractic education. As a result, I knew the landscape well. I was aware of the issues that chiropractors faced in dealing with the quackery epithet often thrown at them by those who knew little or nothing about the preparation and definition of the profession. Chiropractic was also the frequent target of other health care professionals who were determined to fight chiropractors for the turf they felt was invaded by these "infidels."

I was also aware of the internal tension within the field. There were chiropractors and chiropractic colleges that were known to be dedicated to the proposition that the chiropractic adjustment was all that was really needed to treat practically any condition. Juxtaposed to those were the chiropractors and chiropractic colleges that subscribed to the notion that chiropractors could be part of a patient provider team of physicians, physical therapists, and other health care professionals. These so called "mixers" were often held in disdain by the purists.

These internal conflicts were surprising to me, a non-chiropractor. I have been the beneficiary of chiropractic care for over twenty years. But I never knew of these internal divides within the profession. I was happy to be working for an institution that trained men and women to become health care professionals that emphasized self-care and natural healing, two of the tenets of the profession.

As a cancer survivor, I took advantage of the Parker Wellness Clinic and worked with the student interns and their faculty attending doctors. They helped me deal with the post-treatment ailments that hit me hard while I was still in the throes of recovery.

In addition, the schedule of work helped keep me moving and adjusting to my new reality of reduced strength and stamina. My boss told me to take as much down time as I needed to keep my strength up and not to wear myself out. I took those words to heart but did my best to show that I could withstand the daily schedule and not rely on sick days unnecessarily.

I was still using the damned feeding tube during these first weeks, but I did not do any tube feeding during the workday. When traveling, I would take enough of the feeding formula with me to tide me over from meal to meal. I would have to jury-rig a hanging arrangement for the feeding tube to have the gravity pull needed to move the product from the plastic bag down the tube and into my stomach. I had some pretty strange contraptions with the bag hanging from light fixtures and tall lamps, but I managed to make them work. I always tried to put the feeding tube paraphernalia out of sight for fear the housekeeping staff might thing there was something illegal going on.

THE FEEDING TUBE GOES AWAY

After being on the job for about three or four months, my weight stabilized; and I began to put on a few pounds. I credit this to the discipline of getting up, feeding tube, lunch at work, snack at work, feeding tube and dinner at home. My colleagues, especially Angela, did all they could to help me keep putting the calories under my belt. I will never forget how much they helped Melody and me reach the point where I felt it was time to say goodbye to the feeding tube and all the accoutrements.

On our next visit to MDA, we met with our dietician; and she agreed that the time had come for me to get off the tube and rely solely on my oral intake. We arranged to meet with my surgeon and discuss the removal process.

We went to surgeon's area and met her in an examining room. She had me unbutton my shirt and looked at my feeding tube that had been in place for over a year. She explained that we could go the surgical route and have me sedated as they did when the tube was inserted.

Or, she told us, we could do this. Before the last word was out of her mouth, she reached over to my stomach, took the tube firmly in her right hand, and gave it a mighty yank. The tube popped out with the two washers that had kept it in place in my stomach still connected. Some blood began to ooze out of my new belly button.

She swabbed the wound and said that a small amount of bleeding was normal but would stop soon. I thought, *Damn, that hurt a little bit,* as the device came out, but it was over in a moment without all the surgical rigamarole. No stitches were required and the opening in my stomach soon closed with no complications. Now I am the not-so-proud possessor of two belly buttons

Now it was time to really start eating with a purpose. And that purpose was

Image of Melody and Fred Zuker at a meal

not enjoyment but survival. We were told that if my weight began to drop again, there were more feeding tubes that could be installed. I thought that I would be damned if I would put up with that again and resolved to eat and drink as much as I could to keep my weight stable and move the needle up a few pounds.

Eating was still a definite chore with little or no pleasure. I didn't have much of an appetite at all. I made myself eat when we thought it would be best. We tried to make eating as pleasant as possible. We had lots of soups, stews, fruits, and vegetables because that would have the liquid that helped me get the food down. My mouth continued to be dry, making eating anything that was dry almost impossible.

MEAL MINDFULNESS—ENJOY IT WHILE YOU CAN

As I write this I am reminded once again of how important it is to take eating seriously. Food is what sustains us physically and to a large extent, emotionally. Eating is associated with rest in the workday; recreation with friends and family; and enjoyment of taste, texture, and presentation. In short, eating is sustenance and so much more.

When one cannot enjoy the basic sensory pleasures of eating, taste, texture, and satiation, an entire dimension of the human experience is compromised. When swallowing is not something to be taken lightly, eating becomes a chore requiring constant attention to the amount of food taken into the mouth, the texture and liquid content of the food, and when and how to swallow to ensure that the food will not be aspirated. For the swallowing-compromised person, this makes talking while eating even more complicated than it normally is. A working lunch for me to this day is difficult. Trying to talk and chew at the same time can be dangerous if the food is not swallowed carefully.

The upshot is that food and eating have a central place in the human experience and is even more important for the eating-compromised. *We eat to survive, but we also eat to thrive.* Being mindful of that will increase the pleasure of the food and eating experience.

I have learned that lesson the hard way with years now of compromised eating mechanics and enjoyment. It has gotten better incrementally but will never be what it was pre-treatment. Enjoy and appreciate your food, of all kinds, as often as you can. I call it "meal mindfulness," and all of us could benefit from more of it.

A TASTE OF HONEY: FOOD STOPS BEING THE ENEMY

As my recovery went on my sense of taste and production of saliva improved. At one of the follow up visits, I was prescribed Pilocarbine to help with the saliva problem. The drug has definitely helped. I take it three times a day along with Gabapentin which was prescribed to alleviate the peripheral neuropathy that has become part of the new me. More saliva has made the eating process easier and more enjoyable.

I still have no hunger pangs, unlike I did before treatment. Because my swallowing is still imperfect, I tend to take longer to eat and must take smaller bites to make sure the bolus of food can be easily swallowed. Thankfully, some of the taste I had lost has returned, although taste is not nearly as enjoyable as it was pre-treatment. But it is there and what a blessing that is.

Chapter 14: I am a Survivor, so What Does that Mean?

I am a cancer survivor. The medical term for my cancer is oropharyngeal squamous cell carcinoma. In non-medical terms it is a tumor at the base of my tongue. When it was diagnosed at MD Anderson in 2014, it had reached stage four. The stage of the disease was determined by the size of the tumor and the spread of the cancer to some of the surrounding lymph nodes. I immediately began chemotherapy, which had dramatic and painful side effects but hit the tumor hard, essentially removing it from a post-treatment CT scan. This was followed by thirty-three radiation treatments focused on my neck from ear to ear, down to my collarbone.

This was accompanied by more chemotherapy, which we were told would enhance the effect of the radiation.

The last few of the radiation treatments were excruciating and the long-lasting side effects on swallowing, taste, appetite, and dry mouth were profound. These side effects caused me to drastically reduce my caloric intake with the resulting loss of weight. My pre-treatment weight was around 210 pounds. By two months after treatment ended on July 30, 2014, I was down to about 175. My dietician recommended to me and our team of physicians that I be fitted with a feeding tube.

The great news was that the tumor was gone. My wife Melody and I celebrated with hugs, kisses and excited communication to our children and friends who knew of my condition.

We were also required to return to MD Anderson every three months for follow up CT scans, blood work, occasional X-rays, and examinations by my first-rate team of physicians on the MD Anderson staff.

NEW ROUTINES

I am a cancer survivor, but now I must make changes to my normal, pre-cancer routines to continue my recovery. Besides the frequent follow-up visits to MDA in Houston, I still had health issues to deal with.

In addition to the feeding tube and all it involved, I had to exercise my swallowing muscles to prevent the atrophy of the muscles and ligaments of swallowing. I continue to do my swallowing exercises every day.

Another side effect that I noticed not too long after the last of the radiation treatments was a "wattle" or "turkey neck" under my chin. A wattle is defined as "a fleshy, wrinkled, and often brightly colored fold of skin hanging from the neck or throat of certain birds (chickens and turkeys) or lizards" (*Vocabulary.com, nd*).

My version was a pouch that suddenly emerged from the skin under my chin and extended to my neck. It was probably an inch and a half at its droopiest point. At lease it wasn't brightly colored like my face had been. I was afraid that people might mistake me for Senator Mitch McConnell, who sports quite a bit of flesh under his chin. It didn't hurt and felt mushy to the touch, as if it contained fluid.

I went to "Dr. Google" and found that this was probably a side effect of the radiation applied to my lymph nodes. Lymph nodes have no endogenous pumping ability (like the heart functions with blood) to return the lymph fluid from its source in the neck, but through the neck and back to the blood by way of the large veins at the base of the neck. From the head and neck, this is done by gravity. From the limbs and torso, moving the fluid upward is done by the activity of the muscles and joint pumps. When there is an interruption in the ability of the fluid to move properly and to return to the blood stream, there can be a back-up of fluid (edema/swelling) (*Miller, nd*).

I found that there are ways of using massage to encourage the lymph to move through the body. I began using a series of massage movements in the area around my neck and back to encourage the lymph fluid through the pathways of the lymph vessels. Within a few days I saw the wattle begin to shrink. After a week of the massage regimen, the skin under my chin had gone back to normal.

I continue to do the massage treatment daily to make sure the lymph fluid is moving as normally as possible. This is another ritual that has become part of my post-cancer-treatment regimen.

Then there is the care that I must take in eating. I pay close attention to getting the calories and nutrients that I need. I also make sure to eat foods with enough moisture to make it easy to swallow. I pay attention to hydration throughout the day. The challenge is that my appetite is still not what it was, so I must make sure to eat enough. I also take longer for meals and have to plan for this extra time.

It now takes me longer to go through my daily routines. But doing so mindfully helps me keep my cancer fears at bay.

FOLLOW-UP APPOINTMENTS

After treatment is completed, cancer patients are asked to return for follow-up testing and examinations to make sure the side effects are under control and the damned tumor hasn't resurfaced or cancer hasn't cropped up somewhere else.

The first year after treatment, we returned from Dallas to MDA in Houston every three months. During the second year the visits went to every six months. In the third year, if all was well, you might graduate to "Survivor Status." At MDA they tell us that as soon as you are diagnosed with cancer you are a survivor.

That makes a great poster theme, but the reality is that we "survivors" want to get the official word that the cancer has not returned before we flirt with telling family, friends, and the curious that we are survivors. Most people hearing those words think, great, you've beaten this monster. When in fact, the drama goes on for a lifetime as we count our days cancer-free with relish but know that we shouldn't get too cocky. Cancer doesn't seem to like that and may strike you down just to show you who's boss.

These follow-up visits to MD Anderson usually involved an all-day wait for the testing to be completed and the visits with dieticians, audiologists, and dental experts (radiation can have dramatic effects on teeth). It was well known among patients and their families that the MD in MD Anderson stood for "Most of the Day." The final stop on these visits was with a member of the team to review the CT Scan results. These visits rotated among the three MDs on the team.

Every time we went for one of these exams, the sense of dread would gather around us. We knew that recurrence of the tumor was a possibility. As we went through these scheduled follow-up visits and the moment of test-results disclosure drew nearer, Melody and I would occasionally glance at each other and roll our eyes. This was a signal of what we were thinking but did not articulate—*Will this one be okay?*

After the chemotherapy, my team had decided that I should have the radiation regimen even though the CT Scan post-chemo indicated that the tumor was gone, we were told that the radiation would ensure, to the extent possible, that all the cancer-causing cells would be eliminated, thus reducing the chance for a recurrence. It sounded something like an insurance policy against further cancerous attack. We did it and I'm glad we did. But it exacted a high price.

My final stop with the team member to get the results of the CT scan usually started with a medical intern working with the doctor to do a preliminary exam of my mouth and throat. This required the insertion of laryngoscope into my nose and down my throat. The scope included a tiny light and camera that sent a picture of my throat and the site of the tumor to a computer monitor that we watched in real time as I sat in the chair.

Once or twice during these preliminary exams, the intern would say something off-hand like, "Oh, everything on the scan looks good." Often, they made no reference to the results of the scan.

When we got a hint of good news, I would glance at Melody and give her a thumbs up. If there was no indication of good or bad, we would roll our eyes again in that waiting, hyper-vigilant, "Will this fucking test be good or not?" mode.

SURVIVORSHIP—I WANT TO BE ON THAT SHIP

One year ago, after another CT scan with no evidence of recurrence, one of our team doctors told us that I was now moving to "survivor status." This meant that the follow up examinations would take place on a yearly basis, and I would be working with a survivorship team that would be less involved with active treatment than my original team. However, this team would be more easily accessible for the follow-up exams.

This was excellent news to us. This was after two years of follow-up exams. The first year they were every three months. In the second year, every six months. Those tests had been without any evidence of recurrence. Those were the good exams, and we almost began to think of them as routine. But cancer has a way of striking down the haughty. That is why I never said anything dismissive about these follow up visits. Every one of them was about life or death and we knew it.

R. Fred Zuker

Chapter 15: A Long Day at MD Anderson—Again

*Every trip to MD Anderson Post-
Treatment Is Like a Trip to Vegas
–You Want to Keep the Winning
Streak Going.*

AM I STILL A SURVIVOR?

Lucy made it all the way up the stairs by herself this morning. Lucy is our fourteen-year-old Yorkie who weighs in at about three-and-a-half pounds. She is totally blinded by the cataracts that began to cloud her eyes two years ago. I mention this because this little dog's show of courage and determination reminded me of our recently completed drive from Dallas to Houston for me to revisit the MD Anderson Cancer Center for an unexpected and traumatic follow up examination of a spot that appeared on a routinely scheduled survivorship update.

After a year had passed since my designation as "survivor," it was time for us to return to MD Anderson for my first survivorship follow-up examination. This one would include the usual blood work and CT scan with the addition of a chest X-ray. The chest X-ray was now routine. One of my earlier chest pictures had revealed a spot that looked potentially problematic, but it was decided to keep an eye on it in case of any evidence of unwanted development.

This is what I call Stage 6—Secrets of Survivorship. We survivors don't want to do anything that might cause the cancer to return. So, we pay attention to every cancer death we hear or read about and always want to know, *What kind of cancer was it?* Was this the first appearance or a return? We want to know if the cancer that led to death had features like our own.

Like the childish voice that came out at a Catholic service on Good Friday, the only day in the Catholic liturgical year that there is no Eucharistic Mass, when...

(T)he priest loudly intoned, "and Christ dies."

As the gathered worshipers were respectfully quiet at this dramatic moment in the Catholic Paschal (Easter) ritual, this small voice asked. "Did he smoke?"

People always want to know, did he smoke? We survivors want to make sure that people won't be asking that type question about us.

The trip from Dallas to Houston was uneventful and as uninteresting as usual. We arrived at the Jesse H. Jones Rotary House International Hotel in time for me to have my blood drawn in a facility at the hotel rather than first thing in the morning at the hospital.

That wonderful convenience saves sitting early in the morning in the specimen draw waiting room surrounded by many people waiting to begin their round of examinations and meetings. There the mood is usually somber with virtually nothing to lighten the tone.

The next day we went to the imaging waiting room. I signed in for the CT scan and waited to be called. One of the technicians called for me and I went into a room off the waiting area and answered some of the usual questions about medications, allergies, etc.

Then she said she had to start the IV for the contrast dye to be injected for the scan. I told her that I have had many difficulties with IV starts. That I have been told that my veins roll, making it difficult to make the IV puncture. She tried, and it didn't work.

I should have insisted on having a nurse do this procedure. I went back to the waiting room and waited until I was called in for a successful stick by one of the nurses.

After waiting in a holding room for about half an hour, I was taken to one of the CT procedure rooms equipped with the large tubular CT mechanism with the sliding patient platform that moves the patient into the scanning area inside the machine.

I told the technician that I have had difficulties with the injection of the dye if it is put in too quickly. On one of the first such injections, I had what I have heard referred to as a "blowout," where the fluid did not go into the vein but into surrounding tissue at the injection site. She said not to worry, that the fluid flow for a head and neck scan was not that much. When she told me over the intercom that the injection was starting, I felt unusual pain, but it subsided, and I did not call for the procedure to stop.

CT scans are a noisy affair with a lot of loud thumping sounds all around you inside the tube. Patients with claustrophobia issues are often challenged by the close surrounding of the tube and the accompanying noises. The thumping comes in waves and seems to surround you as you are lying perfectly still inside the apparatus. It is disconcerting, but it is over in about twenty minutes or so.

When I came out of the tube and the technician began to work on the injection dressings, she said that some of the dye had leaked out but that enough of the dye had gone in to make the imaging usable. The excess fluid had gathered in a bulge under the skin of my arm next to the injection site. She gave me a cold pack and said it would be absorbed in a few hours.

She then said in the future, I should let them know about this tendency. I thought that is what I had done in this case but decided not to make an issue of it. I was far more concerned about the outcome of the test than a small edema on my arm.

Now is when the waiting begins in earnest. The test has been done and your fate is in the hands of the radiologists who review these tests by the thousands every day. To them, I am sure, mine is just one of many lab images they must review and then forward their findings to the doctors. I wondered, *Do they pause when they see a result that will mean more pain and suffering for the patient? Do they utter or at least think, "Too bad?" Or, is it just another set of data to be analyzed and there is no time for reflection on what this means to a human being, family, friends, the community?*

We went to another area in the hospital that is the home of the head and neck specialists. We have been there many times before and know the waiting areas and where the technicians appear who will escort you into their area to take vitals—weight and blood pressure—before seeing one of our team.

We checked in at the head and neck area and went to the Azalea waiting area. All these areas are named for flowers. After a short wait, our Survivorship Program clinician appeared. She is a nurse practitioner and is devoted specifically to cancer survivors who have been cleared for membership in the exclusive Survivorship Program. She invited us into one of the examining rooms, and I took my seat in the examination chair. Melody took her usual seat in one of the occasional chairs provided for guests.

The NP, who was friendly and professional, told us they were waiting for the CT scan results. She engaged us in conversation about how I was feeling. We told her about some very painful, arthritis-like attacks I had recently experienced in my elbow and wrist. She said she wasn't sure what might be causing that type of symptom.

We had resorted to "Dr. Google" and had found some references to migratory arthritis, an inflammatory condition that might be a precursor to the discovery of malignant tumors somewhere in the body. The reaction, according to Google, was the body fighting the invasion of the cancer cells, thus resulting in the inflammation.

I'm sure that medical professionals are constantly subjected to the online research results of searches done by patients to try and find out more about conditions that are causing concern. We have learned to be skeptical of such research findings but have found that some of the information is quite useful and often reassuring.

I told the NP that I had noticed a slight swelling behind my lower left ear. It was small and a little sore. She palpated the area on both sides of my head and said they felt symmetrical (not alarming) to her.

It was at this time that she stepped out of the room. Perhaps it was a notice on her computer screen that was opened to my complete MDA file that indicated the CT scan results were in.

She returned, sat down, and told us that there was something on the scan that indicated a lesion in the parotid salivary gland area right where I had noticed the lump and soreness.

It is impossible to accurately describe the feeling that sweeps over you upon hearing news like that. I looked at Melody. Her eyes were wide with disappointment, fear, sadness, and most of all, concern for me. I could feel the rush of love and concern from her like a reassuring wave of warmth from a glowing fireplace. I'm sure my pulse quickened, and my blood pressure spiked. My mind went blank except for one term, *Motherfucker!*

I asked the NP if this was something we could watch for any changes and not take any action right now. She paused and said, "Four or five years after the end of treatment is about the time that some recurrence might happen."

That was new information to us. I think we were under the impression that once official "survivorship" status had been reached, it was less likely there would be new or recurring problems. We knew there were no guarantees about new symptoms, but it was still a shock.

The NP said they would recommend an ultrasound examination combined with a needle biopsy aspiration of the suspected area to determine what it was and what next steps might be.

Melody and I looked at each other again and both shook our heads. Melody asked if there was any way that could be done later today or tomorrow, Friday, since we were planning to stay in Houston for the weekend? The NP checked and found out that the first availability for the procedure was on September 13, two weeks from that day.

Again, we shook our heads thinking, *We have to wait two fucking weeks with this hanging over our heads.* That was our only option. We agreed to have the appointment scheduled, and we made reservations at the Rotary House for our unexpected and unwanted return trip to MDA.

The drive back to Dallas was much more tempered than our drive to Houston.

The trip to MD Anderson for these follow-up exams is always fraught with anxious anticipation. The attitude is primarily to get the process completed so we can expel the continuous undercurrent of anxious waiting that exists for a few days before the tests. When the news of the examinations is good, we can relax for at least a short while and let life return to normal. The return trip after good news always seems much shorter. The days leading up to the Houston trips are always reflective and tense.

I learned not to obsess about these tests on the follow-up trips. My attitude was that they were good for us as reminders of what we should be doing and checks on anything that might have happened in the interim that gave us concern.

HAVING CANCER MEANS YOU NEVER FORGET HAVING CANCER

Cancer survivors are constantly monitoring their body and body functioning. If there is a new pain or a sore that doesn't heal on time or just about anything that is unusual, your mind always goes to the *Is this the beginning of something related to the cancer?* place. *Or, is it just one of a hundred things that the body is doing around the clock?*

This hypervigilance is tiring. It often interferes with sleep, and many times I find myself worrying about a nagging cough or post-nasal drainage. Any change in my head and neck area gets my immediate attention.

About once a week I will put my finger down my throat to feel the area where the tumor was located. This is what I did when I first discovered the growth at the bottom of my tongue. I will reach down until the gag reflex kicks in to determine that all that is on my tongue is the rough patch where the tumor used to be. When there is nothing new, I am swept with the feeling that things are okay.

Because of the changes in my ability to generate saliva and difficulty swallowing, I remind myself to be careful about what and how I eat. I am still concerned about keeping my weight up, but the possibility of choking is always there. This has become standard procedure since my bout with the loss of appetite and taste and the onset of dry mouth. I still have virtually no taste and little hunger pangs. Swallowing is still a chore, and I am especially careful of anything that is dry (especially bread in any form or cookies which I have always loved) that might form a clump in my throat. I remind myself to eat, and when I do, to chew solid food at least twenty times.

Since my retirement, keeping my weight has been an even greater challenge. Since retirement, I don't have the scheduled meals, snacks, and evening events that always included food and drinks. Now I am down to about two meals a day on average and far fewer between meal snacks.

When I mention this, people often tell me how lucky I am not to have to worry about too much weight. I would prefer the "Lean Cuisine" problem in a moment compared to the tasteless, joyless, eating experiences I now consider my persistent reality. The old question of "Do you live to eat or eat to live?" has unfortunately been answered in the second case for me.

WAITING TO GO BACK TO MD ANDERSON

The period between the time of the CT Scan on August 30 and our return appointment for the ultrasound and needle biopsy of the left intraparotid lymph nodule on September 13 was a waiting period of infinite uncertainty and anxiety.

As we drove home on I-45 toward Dallas to wait for the biopsy, I told Melody that I thought we should treat this situation as calmly as possible. We didn't know what we would learn on the 13th, and there did not appear to be anything else that was problematic in the CT scan or the chest X-ray.

That was easy to say but very hard to practice. A few years earlier we had been through a similar waiting period when Melody's routine mammogram yielded a result they wanted to biopsy. We had to wait for that to take place, and then there were a few days before we received good news about the results of the biopsy. The difference was I had already had cancer, and we knew what it would mean by hard fought experience if we had to take that treatment path again.

Not a single day passed during this interim period that I didn't go to sleep with the thought of this looming exam intruding on my consciousness. The same effect took place in the morning, except that often I would wake up as early as 4:00 a.m. and not be able to go back to sleep because of thoughts of what this biopsy might reveal.

Having already endured the brutal side effects of chemotherapy and radiation treatment, I could not help thinking about the possibility of being shoved back into that life-changing discomfort and the associated encroachment of depression. I reminded myself that thousands of people go through the same torment constantly. That is small comfort when that sword is hanging over your head. I did not want to go to that place before we knew the results of the exam.

To her everlasting credit, Melody was steadfastly positive about the outcomes of the first round of treatments despite the withering spiral of the side effects.

So, we carried on with our lives and counted down the days for our return to Houston.

BACK TO MD ANDERSON

The day of departure arrived—Wednesday, September 12. The procedures would take place the next day at 7:45 a.m. in the Mays building of the MD Anderson complex.

The long drive to Houston seemed to take less time than usual. I suppose that might have been the dread of what lay in store for us. When you dread getting somewhere or you have allowed too much time, all the lights turn green and the traffic disappears. I always think that must be a cosmic joke, or maybe it is nothing more than perception brought on by anticipatory anxiety. Like when all the lights turn red and the traffic snarls when you are running late.

We checked in at the Rotary House and went to our room. It was around 5:30, and we thought we would go to the restaurant, have an early dinner, and just chill in the room until time to go to bed.

The feeling that afternoon was tense. It was a little like the day before a big football game with a tough opponent that you knew could kick your ass. You played it cool but knew that a lot was riding on your performance, and you wanted to do your best.

The dispiriting thing about cancer is that once you're in its clutches, there is not a damn thing you can do except take care of yourself, go through the treatment, keep your attitude positive, and don't give up hope. There is not going to be a game where you can defeat this terrible foe. In some ways your body is working against you, and the odds are on the side of this silent, implacable enemy.

But, I thought, It ain't over till it's over and we won't know the final score for a while. So, why worry? Tune in to Late Night with Colbert *and hope his monologue will take our minds off the deal for a few minutes.*

I had no dietary restrictions since I was not having anything injected into my vein, as was the usual procedure for the CT scan. There was no blood work required for this procedure. We had to appear at the imaging center in one of the buildings at 7:45a.m.

We arrived at the imaging center a few minutes before the appointment time. I checked in and received the ubiquitous wrist band that is checked many times while one is going through the paces at MDA, where great care is made to ensure the person they are working with is the correct person. During the day I would be asked for my Medical Record Number (MRN) at every stop and by every person in the treatment areas that dealt with me.

A nurse took me back to the ultrasound room after I changed into a hospital-type shirt. I waited for a few minutes, and the ultrasound technician came into the room and introduced herself. She was nice and explained what we would be doing. She told me that she might have to push hard with the ultrasound device to get a good picture. She asked me if I was okay, and I asked if I could go to the bathroom before we began. I had no idea how long this would take. I have always subscribed to the British royal family admonition that whenever you have a chance to go to the bathroom or to sit down—do it.

The examination began with an application of a clear gel to ease the movement of the transducer on my skin. The technician was seated by the bed where I was fully extended with my head raised slightly. She asked me to turn my head to the left as she began moving the transducer over my neck area. Often, as the exam went on, she would make entries on the keyboard display that was placed below the screen.

I couldn't see the screen where the images were displayed. I wondered what she saw that caused her to make an entry. It may just have been the protocol for the procedure.

After about six or seven minutes, she asked me to turn my head toward her, so she could work on the left side of my neck. Under my left ear is where I had felt the slight swelling which is also the area where the lesion was located on the CT scan.

In this position I had a direct view of the screen and what she saw on the images that were sent from the transducer to the computer. I was looking at the inside of my neck. In just a minute or two, she made a pass with the device in the area under my ear. I watched the screen carefully, and then a black spot appeared on the screen.

She stopped and put a cursor on the spot and measured it top to bottom and left to right. As she did this I said, "That doesn't look good."

She responded, "We just have to see what it is."

I had hoped, but didn't even tell Melody, that the damned thing would have disappeared. Over the two-week waiting period I checked the area many times and could not find the swelling again. The soreness had also disappeared. But no, there it was—floating in the gray and black image of my neck tissue. This spot was unmistakably there. But was it malignant?

What an awful word! Malignant, the definition: Tending to be severe and become progressively worse. Regarding a tumor, tending to produce death or deterioration; especially: tending to infiltrate, metastasize, and terminate fatally (*Merriam-Webster, nd*). This is the word that is second only to "cancer" in its profoundly shocking impact on the person receiving the news that this process—produce death and deterioration—is under way in the body.

The appearance of the black spot on the screen reminded me of the "black spot" that was presented to Billy Bones and then Long John Silver in Robert Louis Stevenson's *Treasure Island*. The spot indicated that the recipient had been found guilty of something, or a judgment had been made that was not in their favor. The outcome was often death. The saying "on the spot" is said to have originated from this practice. Here I was "on the spot" electronically. I would have to wait to find out if my spot was the evil, malignant kind or something else, less forbidding.

A young doctor came in to conduct the fine needle aspiration, a guided needle placement procedure to draw some cells from the lesion that was revealed on the sonogram image of my left parotid nodule. The procedure was minimally invasive to the extent that it took a very short time with no pain. The doctor made sure she had enough material needed for the biopsy. She excused herself and hurried away with the tissue sample to be studied.

My technician helped me wipe the gel from my neck and shoulders and told me that the doctor would be back shortly to tell us about the results. I asked her if she could go to the waiting area and ask Melody to come back to the examining room to be with me. She said, "Certainly," and left.

Within a minute Melody appeared at the door. Her gaze at me on the bed revealed the turmoil she was experiencing for us. I have known from the first months after meeting Melody that she possesses a high level of empathy, almost to the point of being "extrasensory." She can anticipate calls or messages that have especially good or bad news. Her psychic connection is especially strong with our twin daughters. It is almost like they converse nonverbally. Melody's sensory powers were at full strength the moment she entered that small examining room crowded with highly impressive, technical, medical diagnostic equipment.

She came to me, took my hand, and gave me a kiss. She sat down without once taking her eyes off me. We waited silently for a few minutes.

Then the young doctor entered the room with a broad smile on her face and said the three words that cancer patients live to hear, "No malignant cells!"

I felt the coiled spring of anxiety suddenly relax. To use sports comparisons, this announcement elicited the feeling you get when you see the football sail between the uprights for the winning score or the basketball snap the nylons with the three-point shot that improbably wins the national championship for the women's basketball championship where we were working in 2007. *Holy shit! We win.*

Melody turned to me with tears in her eyes and, not saying a word, gave me a big kiss and hug.

Even with the elation brought by this news it never left my mind that with cancer there is nothing for certain for very long. But right now is the moment of celebration not the deflationary "Yeah, but what about the next test?"

I gathered my things and changed back to my civilian shirt. We made our way to the waiting room of our original team surgeon.

She is one of the super stars at MD Anderson—and there are many, like Dr. Jim Allison of MD Anderson who was just awarded the Nobel Prize in Physiology or Medicine for his research in the unleashing of the body's own immune cells to carry the fight to the rogue cancer cells before they do irreparable damage.

Our doctor told us how pleased she was with the results of the biopsy. She also said that the finding of a non-malignant cyst was consistent with its location and probably not related to my cancer. She said that had she seen the scan, she would not have called for any follow-up testing. It would have been encouraging to have known that at the time it was discovered two weeks earlier. Nonetheless, the news was very good.

Of course, this drama is replayed with minor differences hundreds of times each week at MD Anderson and other cancer treatment facilities and tens of thousands of times a week nationwide. All of us with cancer are members in the League of Survivors. We are survivors until we die. All of us fight the common enemy constantly. Some with skirmishes of medication, injections, endless needle sticks and electronic scans. Some with major battles of surgery, radiation, and devastating side effects from treatment.

We left the hotel and began our trip back to Dallas. We notified our children of the results. I could hear the "Whoosh" of their relief over the phone, even though it was Melody talking to them in the passenger seat beside me.

We decided to stop for comfort food at a Cracker Barrel along the way. As we waited for our table, we wandered through the aisles of Halloween, Thanksgiving and Christmas stuff for sale. During this interlude, my mind went to the calculation that I have been making regularly for the last four years of cancer treatment—*How many more holidays do I have?* It quickly followed that *I'm going to make the **most** of this one.*

Then it occurred to me that none of us should need a death sentence like cancer to make us aware of how precious every moment is with our loved ones and our life. We should be dedicated to making the most of all those moments and ignore the petty annoyances and distractions that are always present.

Love and thanks to Melody and all our family and friends for being in my life. I will do my best for the rest of my life to deserve all that you have given and are giving me.

This experience Melody and I had was a minor but significant victory. To all my fellow cancer colleagues I send my most profound best wishes as you face your own private dramas. Every day is a chance to build our strength to face what comes, to rejoice at the good. And when it's not so good, to hold fast to family, friends and caregivers.

I love you.

I love life. I am grateful to be able to live it with grace.

Selected References

American Cancer Society. "Cancer Staging" in *American Cancer Society* | Information and Resources about for Cancer: Breast, Colon, Lung, Prostate, Skin. cancer.org. Revised 2015. HTTPS://WWW.CANCER.ORG/TREATMENT/UNDERSTANDING-YOUR-DIAGNOSIS/STAGING.HTML

———. 2019. *Colorectal Cancer Facts and Figures 2017-2019. Atlanta: American Cancer Society.*

———."Medicines to prevent and treat nausea and vomiting." American Cancer Society, cancer.org. Revised February 13, 2017 HTTPS://WWW.CANCER.ORG/TREATMENT/TREATMENTS-AND-SIDE-EFFECTS/PHYSICAL-SIDE-EFFECTS/NAUSEA-AND-VOMITING/NAUSEA-AND-VOMITING-DRUGS.HTML

———."Physical Activity and the Cancer Patient." *American Cancer Society.* cancer.org.,©2019 (Accessed November, 2019). HTTPS://WWW.CANCER.ORG/TREATMENT/SURVIVORSHIP-DURING-AND-AFTER-TREATMENT/STAYING-ACTIVE/PHYSICAL-ACTIVITY-AND-THE-CANCER-PATIENT.HTML.

Barrell, Amanda. "What to know about radiation dermatitis." *Medical News Today.* September 24,2018. Healthline Media UK. medicalnewstoday.com. HTTPS://WWW.MEDICALNEWSTODAY.COM/ARTICLES/323155.PHP.

Bhajan, Yogi. "Quotable Quote" *Goodreads. (author page) (accessed January, 2020)* HTTPS://WWW.GOODREADS.COM/QUOTES/378309-TRAVEL-LIGHT-LIVE-LIGHT-SPREAD-THE-LIGHT-BE-THE- LIGHT

Bronson, Sarah. "Examining side effects specific to each targeted drug" Know More Be More (blog). *University of Texas MD Anderson Cancer Center, mdason.org. August 6,2014.* HTTPS://WWW.MDANDERSON.ORG/PUBLICATIONS/CANCER-FRONTLINE/EXAMINING-SIDE-EFFECTS-SPECIFIC-TO-EACH-TARGETED-DRUG.HOO-158910912.HTML.

CDC. 2018. "Head and Neck Cancers." *Center for Disease Control and Prevention. cdc.gov.* reviewed: May 29, 2018. HTTPS://WWW.CDC.GOV/CANCER/HEADNECK/INDEX.HTM.

Chemocare.com. "Blood Clots and Chemotherapy." *Chemocare.* Cleveland Clinic Health Systems. chemocare.com. *2013(?). (accessed October 2019.)*HTTP://WWW.CHEMOCARE.COM/CHEMOTHERAPY/SIDE-EFFECTS/BLOOD-CLOTS-AND-CHEMOTHERAPY.ASPX.

CREAKYSTAFF. "Describing Your Pain With a 0-10 Pain Scale May Be Messing With Your Treatment.

Here's What You Can Say Instead," *GHLF creakyjoints (blog)*. Global Healthy Living Foundation, creakyjoints.org. August 20, 2018. HTTPS://CREAKYJOINTS.ORG/DOCTOR-PATIENT/PAIN-SCALE-NOT-BEST-WAY-COMMUNICATE-PAIN/.

Cunha, John P., DO, (editor). "Neurontin Side Effects Center." *RxList*. Reviewed October 17, 2018. HTTPS://WWW.RXLIST.COM/NEURONTIN-SIDE-EFFECTS-DRUG-CENTER.HTM.

Drugs.com. "Erbitux Side Effects. drugs.com. updated December 25, 2018. HTTPS://WWW.DRUGS.COM/SFX/ERBITUX-SIDE-EFFECTS.HTML.

Isaacs, Jeremy, and Downing, Taylor. 1998. *Cold War: An illustrated history 1945-1991*. Little Brown & Company, New York.

Martin, Rachel, and NPR Staff. "Remembering the Doomed First Flight of Operation Babylift."Weekend *Edition Sunday, NPR,* National Public Radio. *(radio broadcast)* April 16, 2015. HTTPS://WWW.NPR.ORG/2015/04/26/402208267/REMEMBERING-THE-DOOMED-FIRST-FLIGHT-OF-OPERATION-BABYLIFT.

Mayoclinic.org. "Peripheral neuropathy" *Mayoclinic.org.* May 22, 2019.HTTPS://WWW.MAYOCLINIC.ORG/DISEASES-CONDITIONS/PERIPHERAL-NEUROPATHY/SYMPTOMS-CAUSES/SYC-20352061.

Merriam-Webster, nd. "malignant" *Dictionary by Merriam-Webster*. Merriam-webster.com. (accessed December 2019) HTTPS://WWW.MERRIAM-WEBSTER.COM/DICTIONARY/MALIGNANT.

Mdanderson.org. "Facts & History: Who Was MD Anderson?" *Mdanderson.org*. The University of Texas MD Anderson Cancer Center, *2019,* HTTPS://WWW.MDANDERSON.ORG/ABOUT-MD-ANDERSON/FACTS-HISTORY/WHO-WAS-MD-ANDERSON.HTML.

——- "Know More Be More" (search term/page) (blog). University of Texas MD Anderson Cancer Center. *Mdanderson.org.* (accessed December 15, 2019). HTTPS://WWW.MDANDERSON.ORG/PATIENTS-FAMILY/SEARCH-RESULTS.HTML?Q=KNOW%20MORE%20BE%20MORE&SEARCHTYPE=PUBLICATION&ORIGI N=FILTER#.

Michon, Heather. "What Does It Mean If I Have Rolling Veins?" *myIV.com* (blog). IV.watch. August 31, 2018. HTTPS://WWW.MYIV.COM/ROLLING-VEINS/.

Miller, Matthew, MD. nd. "Lymphedema." American Head & Neck Society – AHNS. (Accessed January 1, 2020) HTTPS://WWW.AHNS.INFO/SURVIVORSHIP_INTRO/TOPICAL_REVIEW-LYMPHEDEMA/.

Online Etymology Dictionary. nd. "malignant (adj.)" *Online Etymology Dictionary. (accessed 2019)* HTTPS://WWW.ETYMONLINE.COM/.

Orlando, Alex. "Building a City of Medicine: The History of the Texas Medical Center." *TMC News* (blog).TheTexasMedicalCenter.tmc.edu.August21,2014.HTTPS://WWW.TMC.

EDU/NEWS/2014/08/BUILDING-A-CITY-OF-MEDICINE-THE-HISTORY-OF-THE-TEXAS-MEDICAL-CENTER/.

Revelant, Julie. "10 ways to get through an MRI or CT scan if you're claustrophobic." *Medical Tech.*, Fox News Network, LLC. June 1, 2015. Updated October 24, 2015. HTTPS://WWW.FOXNEWS.COM/HEALTH/10-WAYS-TO-GET-THROUGH-AN-MRI-OR-CAT-SCAN-IF-YOURE-CLAUSTROPHOBIC.

University of Kansas Cancer Center. "Strong and Stable: Exercises for Core, Strength and Balance." The University of Kansas Cancer Center. *kucancercenter.org*, August 2016. HTTPS://WWW.KUCANCERCENTER.ORG/~/MEDIA/FILES/KUCC/SUPPORT-SERVICES/StrongStableExerciseBookletAug2016.ASHX?LA=EN.

——-"Voice and Swallow: Swallowing Conditions and Treatments." University of Wisconsin School of Medicine and Public Health. *uwhealth.org*, [nd] HTTPS://WWW.UWHEALTH.ORG/VOICE-SWALLOW/SWALLOWING-CONDITIONS-AND-TREATMENTS/11457. –SEE ALSO: HTTP://WWW.UWHEALTH.ORG/VOICE-SWALLOW/VOICE-AND-SWALLOWING/11279. –SEE ALSO: HTTPS://WWW.UWHEALTH.ORG/VOICE-SWALLOW/SWALLOWING-TREATMENTS/26132.

Vocabulary.com. "Wattle." Vocabulary.com Dictionary. *Vocabulary.com*, [nd]. HTTPS://WWW.VOCABULARY.COM/DICTIONARY/WATTLE.

R. Fred Zuker

BOOKS BY R. FRED ZUKER

The Zuker Memoirs Series on Amazon.com

The Dark Angel Turned Away (*coauthored with Ray F. Zuker*)

Standing Tall and Looking Good: *One Soldier's Life and Lessons Learned from 1968-1971*

Grace with Meals: *A Personal Experience of Cancer's Discovery, Treatment, Recovery; & The Truth of Life It Bestows*

Other books by R. Fred Zuker

Peterson's Guide to College Admissions:
Everything you need to know to successfully complete the college admissions process in the 1990s (5th Ed. © 1991; 1st Ed. © 1976)

Kaplan Guide to College Admissions (*©1995*)

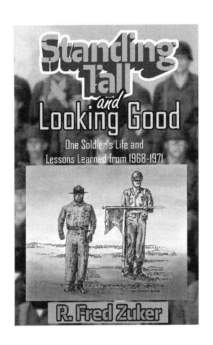

READ THESE BOOKS IN THE ZUKER MEMOIRS SERIES.

EXCERPTS FROM STANDING TALL AND LOOKING GOOD:ONE SOLDIER'S LIFE AND LESSONS LEARNED FROM 1968-1971
(Available on Amazon)

These excerpts were reformatted to match this book.

Chapter 2

IT WAS THE WORST OF TIMES

> *"One, two, three four what are we fightin' for?*
> *Don't ask me, I don't give a damn the next stop is*
> *Vietnam."*
> *Country Joe and the Fish*
> *From their album, "I Feel Like I'm Fixin' to Die*
> *Rag" Released 1967*

1968 was an apocalyptic year – the assassinations of Dr. Martin Luther King Jr in April and Robert Kennedy in June—that left the country shaken and dispirited. The war in Vietnam was continuing to present the nation with the ongoing horror of wartime casualties and increasing uncertainty as to the reason for our involvement in this conflict half the earth removed from America. A good representation of this frustration was the Country Joe and the Fish tune, "I Feel Like I'm Fixin' to Die Rag" that they famously sang at Woodstock to a tumultuous, if slightly inebriated, celebration by the nearly 500,000 people of the Woodstock Nation…

...

Chapter 3

REPORTING FOR DUTY

THE THINGS WE THOUGHT WE NEEDED TO CARRY

I loaded my carefully selected personal belongings into the car for the ride to Knoxville and my trip to basic training at Fort Campbell, Kentucky. I had done a little research and knew that Fort Campbell was the home the 101st Airborne Division, the famous Screaming Eagles of WWII fame, including the defense of Bastogne during the Battle of the Bulge. I wasn't sure what that fact would mean to the basic training program, but I figured it was safe to say that the culture of the place would reflect the hard-nosed, no-nonsense attitude that was the hallmark of the airborne troops who wore their dress uniform pants bloused (tucked) into their meticulously spit-shined jump boots and proudly displayed the airborne insignia on their caps and their uniform shirts. These guys were tough, and they wanted everyone to know it. Their esprit de corps was the highest. They were proud to be airborne tough, and the "straight-legged," non-airborne troops were simply not as good and were begrudgingly tolerated.

When we arrived at the Induction Center, I found the dispersal location for orders and headed toward the bus pick-up point. I bid farewell to my father who had dutifully driven me to Knoxville. His parting words were basically do your best and stay in touch with your mother.

My dad had served in WWII as the senior pilot in a B-24 and B-17. He and his crew flew combat missions out of East Anglia in England. They were one of the few crews that completed twenty-five combat missions and survived. He led his crew of ten through horrific aerial combat engaging the fanatic Luftwaffe fighters and flying through storms of anti-aircraft fire. He didn't talk much about his war time experiences until later in his life when he and I worked on his WWII memoir. I think he was secretly proud of my service in the military. As the oldest, I was the only one of the four of us brothers who did serve. No problem with that fact. It was just the way things turned out.

My mother and I were particularly close. She was not pleased that I was going into the military. But she was resigned to it because, like football, it was what a guy was supposed to do. We were at war, a war that was increasingly unpopular, but I don't recall one word at home questioning the justification for the war. Nor was there discussion about the possibility of me doing anything to delay or avoid the call to duty. I never made plans for a trip to Canada or checked on my need for braces on my teeth or considered the possibility of marriage (although marriage deferment had ended in 1965). I was bound to go, and there at the curb were buses waiting to take me and hundreds of others to basic training. This would be an episode of my life that no number of push-ups or bench presses would have adequately prepared me to endure.

The bus was going to be full, so I took the first empty seat I saw. In the window seat was a nice-looking guy, a little overweight but with a becoming, welcoming smile. He immediately introduced himself. His name was Bob Jameson from Cleveland, Tennessee, not far from Chattanooga. We compared notes on Chattanooga and people we might know. Bob said, "Hey man what do you do?"

"I'm fresh out of college and one step ahead of the Draft Board," I answered.

Bob told me he was an Emergency Medical Technician, EMT. He rode the ambulances and rescue vehicles to accidents and illnesses and delivered first aid and stabilization to people having suffered injurious trauma or strokes and seizures.

He asked me if I wanted to see something gross that he had encountered on one of his emergency auto accident calls. He said, "Check it out. This wrecked car caught fire, and the driver was caught in the car and burned to death. Look at this picture". He worked his wallet out of his hip pocket and pulled out a small photograph of a burned body on a stretcher.

The captivating feature of the photo was the size of the testicles on the victim. I exclaimed, "Holy shit. His balls are as big as basketballs."

Bob told me they had swelled in the heat. This was obviously not a great way to go. Bob said, "I have seen some serious shit on this job. After basic I am going to Fort Sam Houston in San Antonio, Texas, to take the training to be a medic." Bob added, "Those guys are bad asses." Everybody likes them and counts on them when they are in the shit (combat).

Welcome Trainees You're in the Army Now

The bus made its way from downtown Knoxville to Hopkinsville, Kentucky, the town nearest to Fort Campbell. In 1968 Fort Campbell was a prime training site for the new soldiers. The U.S. Army Training Center processed tens of thousands of young men on their way to active duty. I don't think any of the guys in my training company made it to town. But we all knew it was there, and I imagine more than one AWOL used Hopkinsville to make their escape from the rigors of basic training when they became unbearable. The basic training cadre referred to it as "Hop-town." I'm pretty sure the bawdy attractions of

Hop-town, many of which were off limits, played into one of the dramas that would plague us poor trainees during the next nine weeks.

After a ride of a few hours from Knoxville, we pulled onto the base. It was impressively large and bustling. Army green vehicles of all sizes were everywhere. The ubiquitous Jeeps were weaving through traffic with uniformed men looking bored and nonchalant. Hell, they were riding in Jeeps. Not humping it in formation like so many of these trainee newbies we could see from the bus. The giant "Deuce and a Half" trucks were also in great numbers, lumbering slowly, belching smoke, and growling through traffic demanding their right of way. We were just the green fodder for this training facility, trundling along in our candy-ass civilian buses. We were the raw material. Henceforth, during our time at Fort Campbell we would be referred to as "Trainees."

And that is what we were, Trainees. There to be trained, inculcated with the standard operating procedures of what could accurately be called one of the most complex organizations in the world. I probably imagined this, but as we made our way down the crowded streets toward our "Welcome to Fort Campbell" location, the GIs walking along with Coca Colas in hand would look up and assume the expression that bespoke, "Look at those poor fuckers. They have no idea what is waiting for them." If that is what they were thinking, they were right.

We arrived at a large building with a small portico and a neatly lettered sign that said, "Welcome to the United States Army, Fort Campbell, Kentucky, Home of the Combat Arms Group." Standing around the disembarkation area were the cadre of training sergeants. They were lounging and smoking. Some were smiling, others laughing; and a few were standing sullenly checking their watches like they had some better place to be. In fact, they were probably thinking, "Damn, I won't get out of here for another two hours." All the drill sergeants were dressed in green army fatigues. They were wearing utility belts and the mandatory wide-brimmed, "Smoky Bear" hats, a little darker green with the US Army symbol in brass attached above the brim. They wore a Training Center badge on the right breast pocket of their blouse, and all had a brass whistle on a chain attached at the top buttonhole of their blouse and hooked through the buttonhole on their left breast pocket. But there was one of the training cadre personnel that immediately commanded our attention.

STAFF SERGEANT (SSGT.) AND FIELD FIRST SERGEANT (FFS) DERICK COLLINS TAKE US TO OUR STRAC LEADER

SSgt. Collins was the Field First Sergeant (FFS), which meant he oversaw the NCOs who comprised the training staff. The company First Sergeant had responsibility for the non-training organization of the company. But the FFS oversaw virtually everything to do with our basic training experience. Everyone in the cadre, with one exception, proudly wore the Combat Infantry Badge above the shirt pocket on his left side. This meant that each had seen combat in Vietnam. FFS Collins had this badge. He also had the parachute insignia meaning he was airborne qualified. FFS Collins also wore the unmistakable yellow and black horse head insignia of the First Air Cavalry Division, better known as the First Air Cav.

The First Air Cav was one of the most decorated units of the Vietnam war. They fought in most of the major battles of the war from the Battle of IA Drang in 1965 to the Battle of Hue in 1968 during the TET offensive. FFS Collins had probably seen some serious shit.

He stood about six feet tall and weighed around 210 pounds. He was trim and muscular. He was squared away. He was "STRAC." According to the Urban Dictionary, the acronym *means STRictly ACcording to regulations.* That was only part of the meaning of the term. To us in the Army in the 60s STRAC meant you had your shit together, always. Things were in their place and your gear was in top shape and you were ready to move out at any time. FFS Collins was the epitome of STRAC. As an example, his fatigues were always pressed with sharp creases in the trousers. Somehow, he accomplished this in the 90 plus degree heat and comparable humidity of summer in southern Kentucky.

We found out later that SSgt. Collins had played football for one of the base teams in the Army. We heard that these teams were tough as hell and played the game like there was no tomorrow. For many that would turn out to be true if they were later posted to Vietnam. SSgt. Collins was also a bouncer at the Fort Campbell NCO Club. This position required steady nerves, a certain intimidation element to dissuade from violence inebriated soldiers who might have just returned from the insanity of Vietnam, and the brawn to handle situations that required physical intervention to keep the damage under control. We came to learn that the FFS possessed all these traits. SSgt. Collins was the highest-ranking NCO African American in the training cadre. That would take an interesting turn during one training day encounter. He was indisputably in charge. Even the first lieutenant commanding officer of the company deferred to the FFS. Field First Sergeant Collins was a stone cold badass. He didn't need to tell anyone that he was. Just the way he stood at attention in formation let you know he was not a man to be fucked with.

DEAD WEEK

TAKING THE CIVIL OUT OF CIVILIAN

No explicit training takes place during dead week, zero week. It is the time when the brand-new inductees receive their gear and take care of other activities necessary to join the US Army. The first implicit lesson we learned was about the endless lines that we must endure all day long. The comment often made about the Army is all you do is "Hurry up and wait." That lesson was permanently imprinted during dead week. But we had nothing else to do but wait – for everything from clothes to grub.

One of those classic requirements was the GI haircut…

EXCERPT FROM THE DARK ANGEL TURNED AWAY

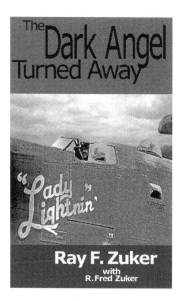

This excerpt was reformatted to match this book.

Prologue

In the year 1942, World War II was gaining momentum, with all its horror and waste. The propaganda of the time left little doubt that every patriotic American should join the effort to rid the world of the devils that had perpetrated this litany of atrocities. This was the situation in which I found myself. Nothing else would do but to become part of the great adventure, and perhaps cloak myself in some bit of glory.

This war was quite different from the military excursions of later years. The enemy was clearly identified; the cause was just; and the true and brave would be triumphant. As with most young men of my generation, I gave very little thought to the potential dangers of war. Reflection before action would come with age and experience. It was time for action with little thought to the consequences that would remain with me all my life.

THE SCENE SHIFTS TO THE SUMMER OF 1987.

I am now a veteran of that long-ago conflict of 1942, a mature 64 years of age. An observer might say I was content with my lot in life; or perhaps it was simply that time had dulled the need to fashion any change in my life. "If it works don't fix it," might have been my motto. I realized my days of instigating change and tilting at windmills were finished.

It was about this time I noticed my body giving me strange signals about something gone awry. Now, a man of mature years shouldn't expect to feel well all the time. However, I had become concerned with nausea and a dull throbbing in my abdominal region. One day I noticed a disturbing, hard lump in my lower abdomen. Early the next morning I went to see my doctor who suggested an immediate sonogram to confirm his diagnosis.

I saw my doctor coming down the hall with his white coattails flying, and I thought, "The news is not going to be good." The sonogram revealed a most urgent problem, what physicians call a "Triple A," an abdominal aortic aneurysm, nine centimeters in length.

If an aneurysm of this type and size ruptures, the patient will be dead in a matter of about two minutes. I was promptly installed in a hospital room, and preparations were made for an emergency operation which was to begin at 4:00 p.m. that day.

I sat alone for a moment during a lull in the preparations and felt a strange but oddly familiar sensation take hold of me. It was an intense moment of unnerving déjà vu. In a rush it came to me; this was the way I felt before my twenty-first bombing mission, the one to Magdeburg, Germany, on August 5th, 1944, almost exactly 43 years earlier to the day.

But why Magdeburg? Even now at crew reunions we rarely refer to that particular mission. There was no doubt that it was a tough mission. The facts are noted in my diary and the records of the Group Historian. But what was there about it that made it sacrosanct for me and my crew?

As I sat waiting for my appointment with the knife, I began to replay in my mind the events of that day which began in a place 4,000 miles away in the lush, green, English countryside. In a dire emergency, time does not heed the 60-minute clock. The events of an entire day can flash through the mind in a matter of seconds. It happened to me as I recalled the details of that half-forgotten mission to Magdeburg. I was startled by the parallel between this day in 1987 and that day in 1944 when my crew and I challenged the fates over Nazi Germany.

That time in 1944 came back to me easily in vivid detail. That August day was clear and bright in East Anglia, England, where the 486th Heavy Bombardment Group was headquartered. At the briefing that morning, we were told there would be clear weather all the way. We would have air cover to the target and back, even though by this time the Luftwaffe had been pretty well neutralized except for sporadic efforts in times and places of their choosing.

Our greatest fear was the heavy and accurate anti-aircraft fire the Germans were now employing. A clear day would make their tracking easier. Fuses could be set well in advance of aircraft arriving in the area so that the barrage could be ten times deadlier than if they had to depend on the radar of the time. The thought of that merciless flak bursting in the skies filled our dreams with dread.

We never spoke of that mission and now I remembered why.

Get these books on Amazon.com. See:

HTTPS://WWW.AMAZON.COM/AUTHOR/RFREDZUKER

Aphorisms on Various Topics

The Truth of Life that Cancer Bestows

Leadership:

You don't really know if you're a leader until you've been tested and failed.

Leadership is about one thing only – yourself.

Great leaders make great leaders.

Leaders who stop learning are lost.

Teamwork is another word for leadership that works.

Team leaders can be dream makers.

Leading by example beats leading by demand every day.

Live life, all of it.

A leader should always remember that nothing is worth doing that will sully her/his reputation.

A good reputation is one thing that money can't buy.

Be true to yourself as a leader. Don't try to be someone else and never be a bully.

Bullying creates enemies for a lifetime. Don't do it.

Not getting the help you need when you need it is a bigger mistake than going it alone and failing.

A sense of humor for a leader can diffuse, infuse, and save the day.

The best form of humor is self-effacing.

Bragging is a barrier. Don't do it.

Every leader has a team. It may be a team of one (yourself). The others will come when you are ready.

The leader takes every success as a testament to the overall effort of the team.

The leader is the motivator of the team, but the team must perform as one.

Every leadership experience contains valuable lessons. The trick is to find them and apply them to the benefit of the team.

Building team unity is an ongoing project. Every activity that is shared by team members is a chance to build team integrity, effectiveness, and camaraderie from break room to board room.

If the team succeeds – hurray for the team. If the team fails, the leader takes responsibility.

Team building leaders take pleasure in everyone doing well, especially those who are struggling.

Helping team members improve is the highest order of leadership.

The leader learns from every activity, win or lose.

When faced with a no-win situation, the leader must choose the course of action which causes the least damage and the greatest good.

Leadership is at its best when the leader empowers and elevates the team.

Number 2 in GWM

Cancer and The Truth of Life It Bestows:

Having cancer means you never forget having cancer.

A diagnosis of cancer is a doorway to self-discovery.

Having cancer shines a powerful spotlight on what's important and what isn't.

Cancer slows time to one morning at a time, one afternoon at a time, one night at a time, one day at a time, one hour at a time.

Cancer teaches you to live life – all of it.

When you eat, the meal is yourself (Zen proverb, A 2020 Day-at-a-Time Calendar)

Don't take a pain-free, comfortable sleep experience for granted. Restorative sleep is especially important for cancer sufferers.

Sleep is the repose that recovers what is lost by STRESS and gives strength for the unknown of waking up.

Number 1 in GWM

Stages of the Acceptance of Cancer:

1. *Disbelief or I can't believe this is happening to me?*

2. *Why is this happening to me? It's not fair.*

3. *I Have cancer - one day at a time.*

4. *Treatment trauma*

5. *Body Breakdown*

6. *Healing – recovery from treatment*

7. *Being a survivor - one day at a time*

Number 3 in GWM

Stress:

Stress is literally sickening.

Worrying doesn't help. Unknit your brow and mindfully relax. Tell yourself, "I will do my best and stop hurting myself."

The worry train is constantly in motion. Pull the emergency handle and when you stop look out the window at the scenery.

Knowing what's important and what's not, may take a life time to learn. By the end it's too late to have any benefit. Slow down and do it now.

Stress never sleeps and it won't let you sleep except in meetings when the boss is looking.

Stress makes the simplest task seem impossible.

Stress often sneaks in to install the ache in your head and neck.

About the Author: R. Fred Zuker, Ph.D.

Image of R. Fred Zuker, 2018

Following his enlistment in the US Army, Fred Zuker returned to school to become Dr. Zuker. As of today, he has 47-years'experience in higher education administration at Duke, Tulane, and other universities and colleges and has been in private practice as an educational consultant. Today he is retired and lives in Dallas, Texas.

In addition to his academic papers and presentations, Dr. Zuker wrote one of the first books on the college admission process, *Peterson's Guide to College Admission: Getting into the College of Your Choice.* He co-authored his father's memoir *The Dark Angel Turned Away,* which was self-published in 1989 and revised with additional content by Fred for ebook publication in 2019. In 2018, he published a memoir of his own US Army experiences, *Standing Tall and Looking Good: One Soldier's Life and Lessons Learned from 1968-1971,* available as a Kindle ebook. This book is his memoir on his cancer experience, *Grace with Meals: A Personal Experience of Cancer's Discovery, Treatment, Recovery; And the Truth of Life It Bestows.*

Dr. Zuker holds an AB (called B.A. at some institutions) in history, M.Ed. in counseling and a Ph.D. in counseling psychology from Duke University.

Dr. Zuker has hosted a weekly movie review radio program *Focus on Film,* a radio program *Education Today,* and co-hosted with Melody Zuker a weekly radio show *Parent Talk.* He wrote a monthly newspaper column on parenting.

Dr. Zuker played varsity football at Duke, served in military intelligence in the US Army, holds a black belt in Tae Kwon Do, has run four marathons, and has survived a bout with cancer. He and his wife Melody are avid movie buffs and loving grandparents.

Dr. Zuker continues to write and will be posting essays and book snippets on the blog *Books and Authors,* where you can also find news of future publications.

Visit Dr. Zuker's author page on Amazon:

HTTP://WWW.AMAZON.COM/AUTHOR/RFREDZUKER

Made in the USA
Columbia, SC
23 June 2022

62126843R10089